FAN

'That was just so incredible!' declared Jessamy. 'The way they use their whole body – the way they express themselves! It couldn't be more different from the ballet! It makes ballet seem almost – ' she searched for the word ' – almost like – like *tinsel*. Like – froth! As if it doesn't have any substance. This is all earthy, and bloody, and – and primitive!'

Jessamy talked, excitedly and non-stop, all the way to Chiswick. Karen said very little beyond the odd 'Mm' or 'Ah,' but then she was not given much opportunity. It wasn't until the cab had turned into her road and they were nearly at her gran's house that she said carelessly, 'Maybe we should go again.'

Jessamy was definitely going to go again. 'But I thought you agreed with Mum that it was only glorified tap?'

Karen's cheeks glowed pink in the semi-darkness. *Now* what was she blushing for?

Other books by Jean Ure

Dancing Dreams series
Star Turn
A Dream Come True

The Peter High series
Jo in the Middle
Fat Lollipop
Bossy Boots
Jam Today
The Matchmakers

Hi There, Supermouse!
Nicola Mimosa
If it Weren't for Sebastian
Always Sebastian

Jean Ure was born in Caterham, Surrey, in 1943, and educated at Croydon High School and at the Webber-Douglas Academy of Dramatic Art. She had her first book published when she was fifteen and has been writing ever since. She changed from adult fiction early in her career and is now one of the country's most popular writers for children and young adults. She is the author of the 'Peter High' series, set in an all-girl comprehensive, as well as of many other critically acclaimed novels, several of which, including *Hi There Supermouse*, utilise her theatrical background. *Star Turn* and *A Dream Come True* are the first two novels in the 'Dancing Dreams' trilogy.

Jean lives in a Queen Anne house in Croydon with her husband, actor Leonard Gregory, six dogs and two cats. Her interests include reading, listening to music and walking. She is a keen supporter of animal rights.

Fandango!

Jean Ure

RED FOX

A Red Fox Book

Published by Random House Children's Books
20 Vauxhall Bridge Road, London SW1V 2SA

A division of Random House UK Ltd
London Melbourne Sydney Auckland
Johannesburg and agencies throughout the world

Copyright © Jean Ure 1995

1 3 5 7 9 10 8 6 4 2

First published by Hutchinson Children's Books 1995

Red Fox edition 1996

Printed and bound in Great Britain by
Cox & Wyman Ltd, Reading, Berkshire

RANDOM HOUSE UK Limited Reg. No. 954009

Papers used by Random House UK Limited
are natural, recyclable products made from wood grown in
sustainable forests. The manufacturing processes conform to
the environmental regulations of the country of origin.

ISBN 0 09 925111 6

1

'Hm!' Miss Fane's forehead puckered itself into a frown as she adjusted the weights on the weighing machine. 'That's another half kilo you've put on, Jessamy.'

Miss Fane stood back, critically raking Jessamy with eagle-eyed gaze. Jessamy squirmed. She pulled in her stomach, tucked in her tail, uncomfortably aware that Miss Fane was not the only one subjecting her to scrutiny. All the rest of the class were there, either awaiting their turn in fear and trembling or lolling complacently, having already been through the ordeal.

Ginny Alexander, coming as she did right at the beginning of the alphabet, had not only been through the ordeal but had triumphantly survived it. Miss Fane had even uttered words of encouragement.

'Well done, Ginny! You've managed to maintain the same weight since almost the beginning of term. You see, it's not so difficult, is it? You only have to be sensible about things.'

Ginny, now, was sitting there in an almost unbearable glow of self-righteousness, legs sprawled out before her, glorying in the fact that her closest rival had put on yet another half kilo.

'Some people just can't seem to maintain a stable weight . . . they go up and down like yo-yos.'

Not even up and down, thought Jessamy, gloomily. Just *up*.

'Poor Jessamy! Miss Eldon always did say she had a big tail.'

Of course, Jessamy couldn't be certain that that was what Ginny was thinking, but it probably was. The world of ballet was so competitive that it was virtually impossible not to exult in another's downfall. Only the very nicest people, such as Karen, never seemed to gloat or suffer the agonies of jealousy that assailed the rest of them. Maybe that was because Karen didn't need to.

Jessamy sighed as she stepped off the weighing machine.

'Yes! You may well sigh,' said Miss Fane. She looked at Jessamy, severely. She was even stricter on matters of weight than Miss Eldon had been. She said that now was the time, when they were approaching young womanhood, to lay down good eating patterns. Good eating patterns, said Miss Fane, would stay with them for the whole of their lives.

But I have good eating patterns! wailed Jessamy, inside herself. How often did she pig out on chips and bars of chocolate? Never! Well, hardly ever. Perhaps just now and again. Just occasionally. Like if she was absolutely starving and needed something in a hurry, or maybe if she'd gone somewhere with Susan and Sheela. (It was all right for those two: they could eat whatever they wanted. They weren't at ballet school.) One ought not, thought Jessamy, to become *obsessed*. Why, it was even what Miss Fane herself said!

'What are we to do with you?' Miss Fane prodded at one of Jessamy's thighs. (Jessamy was sure she heard Ginny titter.)

'I am the last person,' said Miss Fane, 'to advocate an obsession with diet. But that is the whole point of laying down good eating patterns! Once you have established a good eating pattern, there is no need to become obsessed. But it is simply no use stuffing yourself with excess calories one day, then starving yourself the next in the hope of making up for it. That is neither sensible nor healthy – and nor does it achieve its purpose!'

Miss Fane smacked at Jessamy's backside. Jessamy hung her head. It was all very well railing on, as she frequently did, about not being able to eat the same things normal people do, but ballet dancers weren't normal people. Susan and Sheela had informed her of this several times, and Jessamy was reluctantly beginning to think that it was true. Look at the life they led in the Company! Nothing but sweating and straining from morning till night! When was the last time her brother Saul had been injury-free? Pulled hamstrings, stress fractures, tendonitis, torn ligaments ... half the corps de ballet permanently on starvation diets, the other half looking like resur- rected skeletons. It was crazy, thought Jessamy. This whole thing was crazy!

Crazy perhaps, but it was what she had chosen. She couldn't imagine ever doing anything else, even if it did mean Miss Fane prodding and poking at her in front of the whole class and Ginny Alexander sniggering.

'I shan't labour the point,' said Miss Fane, 'but if Ginny can do it, I'm sure you can.'

That was a mean trick! Ginny was positively *smirking*.

For lunch that day, Jessamy pointedly ate one apple, one carrot, and a plain yoghurt. Karen looked at her, anxiously.

'I don't think Miss Fane meant *starve* yourself.'

'I'm not starving myself.' Apples might be boring and carrots were rabbit food, and plain yoghurt tasted like regurgitated yuck, but nobody could deny that it was healthy.

'You could have had soup,' pleaded Karen. 'Or a salad, or a sandwich.' That was the trouble with Jessamy: she never did anything by halves. 'I don't think you need to go on a diet, anyway. Half a kilo isn't anything.'

'Yes, it is! It's this – and this – and *this*.' Jessamy pinched at herself disdainfully. 'They're all half kilos, and they've all got to go!'

Sexist, Sheela said it was, worrying about the odd little bulge here or there (Sheela, of course, being as thin as a length of clothes-line; no shape at all). Sexist it might be, thought Jessamy, determinedly chomping on her carrot, but who wanted a fat Giselle? Who wanted a fat Albrecht, come to that? It wasn't sexist, it was just the way things were in the world of ballet.

'Some people have an unfortunate tendency to put

10

it on.' Ginny smiled as she dug into her baked potato with cheese topping. 'Especially round the hips and thighs.'

Jessamy glowered. She knew for a fact that Ginny herself had a tendency to put it on because her cousin Valentine, whom for a short time Jessamy had gone out with, had told Jessamy so. But as Miss Fane had said, if Ginny could crack it, so could Jessamy.

'You don't want to get anorexic,' warned Maggot, more properly known as Margaret Moorhouse. Maggot herself had once been decidedly dumpy, but had miraculously, without any effort at all, and practically overnight, become transformed into a creature positively elfin. 'Look what happened – ' she lowered her voice – 'look what happened to Carolyn.'

A silence fell upon the table. They didn't as a rule talk about Carolyn. She had been one of their year's most promising dancers and nobody had really noticed that she was gradually fading away to nothing until one dreadful day when she wasn't there any more. It had been Maggot (it was always Maggot) who found out that she had been sent home and was only going to be allowed back when she had gained what Miss Eldon considered to be 'a reasonable amount of weight.' She never had come back, and not even Maggot had been able to find out what had happened to her.

Carolyn's fate was one which hung over them all. It was like walking a tight-rope, Jessamy sometimes thought. The pressure was on them to be thin – but not *too* thin. Too thin and you were suspended; too

11

fat and you were thrown out. So it had to be better (she held her breath as she tipped a spoonful of regurgitated yuck down her throat), it had to be better to err on the side of thinness, because that way you were at least given a second chance.

'Carolyn never used to eat lunch at all some days.' Nella Stevens said it in tones of wonderment, as if the realisation had only just burst upon her, which possibly it had. 'She just used to sit and drink water.'

'Yes, well, there you are.' Jessamy banged down her empty yuck pot with a flourish. 'That's just stupid. I couldn't ever get like that. I sometimes seriously wonder,' she said, 'if there's something wrong with my metabolism ... I mean, I only have to *look* at a Mars bar, practically, and I feel like going berserk and eating half a dozen of them ... I mean, once I start I just can't *stop*. I don't think that's normal,' said Jessamy, 'do you?'

A chorus of groans all about the table assured her that it most certainly was.

'I once ate three Crunchie bars,' said Karen, wide-eyed and astonished at her own greed. 'One after the other, just like that!'

'Oh, well! You!' said Jessamy.

Karen was one of the lucky ones: she could eat an entire sweetshop full of Crunchie bars and not put on so much as a gramme. Once upon a time, when she and Karen had been almost exactly the same size, Jessamy had been patronising enough to consider it a pity Karen was so very fair, since there was no denying that blondes didn't come across the foot-lights anywhere near as well as brunettes; at least,

Jessamy didn't think they did. Now she could only look and marvel, and wonder how it was that at the age of almost sixteen Karen could still have the body of a twelve-year-old whilst Jessamy was bursting out all over. And especially my *hips*, thought Jessamy, venomously. Her hips were disgusting; like great panniers.

'I'm surprised,' said Ginny, 'that your parents don't say anything. I mean, considering.'

She didn't say considering what; she didn't have to. Everyone knew that Jessamy's parents were Ben Hart, the choreographer, and Belinda Tarrant, ex-prima ballerina with City Ballet. It was a bit of a sore point with Ginny, though no one could ever accuse Jessamy of bragging. She certainly never flaunted the fact that she came from a famous family.

'Do you think your mother hasn't noticed?' said Lorraine, who was Ginny's best mate.

'Noticed what?' said Karen, leaping immediately to Jessamy's defence and only making matters worse.

'Well – ' Lorraine shrugged.

'Noticed rolls of *fat*.' It was Jessamy who leapt in. Better to say it oneself than allow Ginny the opportunity. 'No, she's been too busy drooling over the new baby.'

Her second grandchild, supplied by courtesy of her elder daughter. Funny to think Mum had been so mad when Jacquetta gave up dancing to get married and start a family, and now here she was as gooey-eyed as anyone.

Thank heavens for Jack, was what Saul said. It was true that if Mum waited for Saul to produce

13

grandchildren she would wait for ever; while as for Jessamy, she certainly didn't intend sacrificing her career for the sake of horrible little wizened bald things that puked and yelled and made messes in their nappies, thank you very much! If you asked her, Mum was going seriously soft in her old age.

'Look, is anyone coming to Simon's party next weekend?' said Ginny, changing the subject.

Lots of people said they were; one or two, regretfully, said they couldn't because they lived too far away. Karen didn't say anything and no one expected her to. Karen never went to parties, unless dragged there by Jessamy. After four years at ballet school she still tended to be shy; but also, and more importantly, she lived with her gran and didn't like to keep asking for extra money to spend on fares or clothes. Karen's gran had a struggle to make ends meet as it was, and had to let out rooms to supplement Karen's scholarship.

Karen was one of only four scholarship pupils at the school. The big question now was whether the scholarship would continue when she moved up in September to the graduate class. There was no doubt in anyone's mind, other than Karen's, but that she *would* move up. She had long been a favourite of Madam's, and even Ginny had come to accept that for all her seeming insignificance in everyday life, Karen on stage, or even just in a humble studio, inhabited a different world from the rest of them.

'You'll be coming, won't you?' said Ginny. She took it for granted that Jessamy would be there.

Unlike Karen, Jessamy was sociable and loved going to parties. 'Are you going to bring Ant?'

Jessamy shook her head. 'Ant and I aren't together any more.'

'Oh?' Ginny leaned forward, ears flapping. She liked a bit of gossip. 'What happened?'

'Nothing happened. He just got bored with me always saying I couldn't do things.'

Since that terrible time when Madam had nearly thrown her out for going ice skating and injuring herself almost on the eve of a performance, Jessamy had been careful to do nothing which could incur displeasure. She had had a bad shock on that occasion and had learnt her lesson. Anthony had complained it was like going out with a nun.

'It's not natural, the way you people live!'

Maggot sighed. 'That's the problem with having a boyfriend who's not in the ballet . . . they just don't understand.'

'The trouble is – ' Lorraine plunged her fork into her apple crumble. (Apple crumble with custard. All thick and creamy.) 'The trouble *is*, there aren't enough of them to go round. Not if you want one that's in the same business.'

Heads turned, thoughtfully, in the direction of the boys from their own class, sitting in a bunch at a separate table.

'Half of them aren't into girls anyway,' said Ginny.

'John is.'

'Daniel isn't.'

'Nicky is, I *think*.'

'What about Simon?'

15

'Simon isn't.'

'How do you know?'

'You can tell.'

'Are you *sure*?'

Nella giggled. 'Isn't it awful?' she said. 'Discussing them like this?'

'Don't see why.' Ginny stretched, luxuriously, showing off her new streamline figure. (If Ginny could do it . . .) 'They discuss us; I've heard them.'

'What do they say?'

'Usual things . . . which of us might and which of us wouldn't.'

Nella giggled again. 'Which sort were you?'

Haughtily, Ginny said, 'They weren't discussing me.'

Karen was looking bewildered. 'Which ones might what?' she whispered to Jessamy.

'Go to bed with them,' said Jessamy. Karen was so naïve! It came from living with her grandmother. Now, of course, she had turned bright pink. She was always embarrassing herself by asking these questions that a ten-year-old could have answered.

'Poor dear!' Maggot patted her hand. 'She's far too young. She'll learn.'

'Anyway,' said Ginny, 'you're still coming, aren't you? Even without Ant.'

'I can't.' Surreptitiously, under the table, Jessamy pressed both hands to her stomach. It *felt* perfectly flat, but that was only because her hips were so enormous, bulging out like great hillocks on either side. 'I can't,' she said. 'I'm doing something else.'

'Something exciting?' said Maggot.

'Mm . . . quite.'

'What? What are you doing?'

Goaded, Jessamy said, 'Saul's having a going-away party before the Company fly off to Europe.'

She didn't like seeming to boast, but there were times when they pushed her into it. It was hard having a brother who was every young girl's dream. To Jessamy, though she loved him dearly, Saul was just Saul. She had to shake herself to remember that for Ginny and Maggot and the rest he was Saul Hart, *premier danseur*, one of the Company élite.

Ginny's eyebrows, predictably, had flown half way up her forehead.

'Oh! Well,' said Ginny. '*Of course.* There isn't any competition, is there?'

'Couldn't wangle an invitation for me, could you?' said Maggot.

'Mags!' Nella looked at her, shocked. 'Don't presume.'

'I was only joking,' said Maggot.

On the way home, in the tube back to Chiswick, Karen said, 'Are you really going to Saul's party?' (Her cheeks fired up as she said his name; when *would* she grow out of this hateful habit of blushing?) 'Or was it just an excuse not to go to Simon's?'

'Course it wasn't! Course I'm going! So are you.'

'*Me*?' said Karen.

'Well, you've been invited.'

Karen felt her tummy begin to churn in the way that it did when she felt both excited and scared at the same time.

17

'Now, don't go all silly,' said Jessamy. 'You ought to have got over that by now.' Goodness knows, she had seen Saul enough times. He might be devastating just to begin with, but surely the effect had to start wearing off at some stage?

'All those people,' whispered Karen.

'What people? Members of the Company? It's all right, they won't take any notice of us. We can just stand in a corner,' said Jessamy, 'and gorm.'

It was all very well Jessamy saying that, but members of the Company *did* take notice of Jessamy. Some of them had known her since she was a child. Karen would be the one standing in a corner, all by herself and paralytic with nerves.

'Ken will be there,' said Jessamy. 'You like Ken. You can talk to him.'

Karen brightened. Ken was Saul's friend; he was an artist and not anywhere near as high-powered as Saul. Also, Karen didn't happen to have an embarrassing schoolgirl crush on him. She could have reasonably normal conversations without turning into a boiled beetroot. If Ken were there, perhaps it wouldn't be so terrifying.

They left the train at Chiswick and prepared to go their separate ways.

'I'm going to stop off at Safeway on the way home and buy some celery,' said Jessamy. 'Someone told me if you eat celery it actually chews up the calories.'

Karen looked at Jessamy, doubtfully. 'I don't think Miss Fane would want you to do anything drastic.'

'If Ginny can do it –'

'Yes, but Ginny did it gradually. It took her nearly two terms.'

Jessamy tossed her head. 'I can't afford to wait that long!'

It was nearly Easter; next term was when Madam made her selection for graduate class. She certainly wasn't going to select a dancer with huge horrible hips and puddingy thighs.

'I read somewhere,' said Karen, 'that hot baths are good for losing weight . . . they melt the fat, or something.'

'*Truly*?' said Jessamy.

'Well, that's what I read.'

'I'll try it!' said Jessamy.

2

Jessamy dipped an apprehensive toe in the bath. Ouch! It was scalding. She retracted, fast. How hot did it have to be? Not so hot that it cooked you.

She ran the cold tap and tried again. Centimetre by cautious centimetre, she submerged herself. Ow! Oooh! Ah! That was better. That at least was bearable – just about. She looked at her thighs, lying there like great fat sausages in the water. Ugh! Horrible things! It made her feel sick. *Those thighs had got to go.* You couldn't have a dancer twirling across the stage on a pair of fat sausages. It was grotesque.

Jessamy forced herself to sit there, the sweat crawling over her scalp and trickling down her forehead and dripping off her nose until the water had cooled and the sweat felt cold and clammy. The bathroom was so befogged she could hardly see where the towel rail was. The scales, too, had misted over, but on the inside rather than the outside, so she couldn't even wipe them clean and discover how many kilos she had lost. She bet it must be at least two.

Jessamy pulled on her dressing gown, wrapped a towel round her head and went down to the basement kitchen to join her mum and dad for supper. It was unusual for both of her parents to be there.

Her mum was more often out teaching, her dad flying about the world putting on productions for ballet companies.

In the old days, when Jessamy was small and couldn't be left on her own, they had always had an au pair; but now that she was older they just had Mrs Phelps, who came in to clean and cook because neither Mum nor Dad had the time. Mum and Dad couldn't cook, anyway; Mum was even worse than Dad, though Dad was worse than Mum when it came to breaking things. Just recently he had broken the lawn mower, the vacuum cleaner, the washing machine and the video player. Mrs Phelps had been quite cross about the vacuum cleaner and the washing machine. She had said it wasn't any of Dad's business to be touching the vacuum cleaner and the washing machine in the first place, and in future she would thank him to keep his hands off what didn't concern him. Mrs Phelps was one of the few people who could stand up to Dad. Most people were afraid of him, but Mrs Phelps would brook no nonsense. (It was what she always said: 'I shall brook no nonsense!' And she didn't.)

'Good heavens alive, Jessamy!' There was a hint of irritation in Belinda Tarrant's voice. 'What on earth have you been doing?'

'Nothing,' said Jessamy. 'Just having a bath.'

'Well, I advise you to go and take a look at yourself!'

Her mum pointed to the big gilt-framed mirror which hung over the old-fashioned mantelpiece. Jessamy obediently went across and looked. A round, ruby-coloured object stared back at her: her face.

'Like a lobster,' said her dad.

'Lobsters are grey,' said Jessamy. 'It's only when they boil them they go red.'

'Exactly!' Belinda Tarrant pounced. 'Don't you ever do that again! Hot baths are extremely bad for you.'

'Why?' said Jessamy; and as an afterthought she added, 'It's very cruel, what they do to lobsters. They boil them when they're still alive.'

'So I take it you won't be eating them any more?' Her dad indicated the patties that Mrs Phelps had made.

Jessamy struggled for a moment with her conscience. Mrs Phelps' lobster patties were what her dad called 'a gastronomic delight'. It would be very hard never to eat them again.

'Well?' Her dad was challenging her, arrogantly tipping his chair back and balancing against the dresser.

'No,' said Jessamy. (What else could she say?) 'Fish feel pain just the same as we do. I think it's horrible. And why is it bad to have hot baths?'

'It debilitates you,' said her mum.

'I don't feel debilitated.'

'It's bad for the heart. It weakens the muscle.'

'It wouldn't if we had a sauna. Why can't we have a sauna?' Or a jacuzzi; Jessamy fancied herself whirling round in a jacuzzi 'Why don't we have a j – '

'Why don't we have this, why don't we have that! Don't you think you already have quite enough?'

22

'Yes, but if we had a j – '

'Well, we haven't! And we're not going to. Don't argue with me. Just get on and eat your supper.'

Jessamy picked moodily at some salad – but without any dressing, because that was fattening – and managed to roll a bit of french bread into breadcrumbs without actually consuming any of it. Fortunately, since Belinda Tarrant was quite strict about the need for young dancers to eat nourishing meals, her mum and dad were too busy conducting one of their arguments to notice.

Belinda Tarrant and Ben Hart were always arguing; it was because they were both very self-opinionated people. (Saul said that Jessamy took after them but Jessamy didn't think this was necessarily true. She simply had an assertive personality.)

This time they were arguing about whether or not British dancers were becoming fat. Jessamy pricked up her ears. This could be interesting!

'I tell you – ' Ben Hart brought his chair rocketing back to the floor – 'I have never seen such a load of buxom Sylphs in all my life!'

'Just because they don't look like a row of dancing corpses.' Mum snatched angrily at a lobster patty. (Jessamy's mouth watered, but she stood firm. It *wasn't* right to boil lobsters. It was cruel.)

'That's the whole trouble with this business! Men hold the purse strings and want to keep women in their place ... want to keep them looking like ten-year-olds! Of course, the reason is – ' Mum's lip curled, derisively – 'the reason is, they're all terrified. Show them a real woman and they'd run a mile.'

Jessamy's dad banged on the table. 'The reason is, you feminist apology for a female, no one is going to shell out good money to come and see a stage full of coal heavers bulging out of their tutus! And I certainly am not going to make any ballets on a coal heaver. I don't care how famous she is!'

Jessamy leaned forward. 'Is Colleen McBride a coal heaver?'

'No, of course she isn't!' snapped Mum. Colleen McBride was one of City Ballet's leading dancers. She had in the past had classes with Belinda Tarrant.

'Shape like a pumpkin,' muttered Dad.

'Rubbish!'

Jessamy reached out for some cherry tart; then remembered and picked up the mineral water instead. 'Saul always complains she's like a sack of potatoes.'

'That's just Saul being rude. Colleen has a beautiful figure.'

'Pumpkin,' said Dad.

'You only say that because you've just come back from New York!'

'What happens in New York?' said Jessamy.

'Women starve themselves until they look like bags of bones.'

'*All* women?'

'Dancers! It's different for the men, naturally.' Belinda Tarrant's lip curled. 'They're allowed to look like men ... no one wants an anaemic ten-year-old Prince Charming.'

'No, and no one wants a pumpkin-shaped Aurora!'

Mum and Dad surged off again on their rollercoaster; Jessamy was forgotten. She took her glass of mineral water and walked thoughtfully up two flights of stairs to her bedroom. There she locked the door, removed her dressing gown and nightdress and stared at herself critically in the full-length glass which Saul had kindly fixed to the wall so that she could check how fat she was getting.

She *was* fat! It was disgusting! If Dad thought Colleen McBride was a pumpkin, what would he think of his own daughter? And come to that, why had Mum never remarked on it? Generally she watched Jessamy like a hawk – 'You're getting stout! We shall have to watch your diet.'

This time she hadn't said anything; but maybe, upon reflection, that was because Jessamy had taken to wearing long baggy sweaters or T-shirts over leggings. Had she subconsciously been trying to hide all the layers of flab from Belinda Tarrant's ever-watchful eyes? Oh, this was horrible!

Jessamy hurled herself to the floor and began rocking frantically from side to side, trying to break down the fat cells. Why did she have this problem and not Karen? No one else in her family was fat, not even Jack, who had had two babies. Not even Mum, who had had *three*. She would be thrown out, for sure, if she hadn't got rid of these loathsome hips by the end of next term.

Jessamy decided that she would devote the entire summer holidays to the shedding of excess weight. She would take class *every single day* with Mum, and no grumbling about having to work with amateurs; she would run round the block in sweat pants, night and morning; she would take hot baths when Mum wasn't there; and she would eat nothing but raw fruit and veg. – and talking of veg, where was that celery she had bought?

She dug it out of her bag, rushed along to the bathroom to wash it, and spent the rest of the evening glumly munching as she watched a video of Balanchine ballets danced by American women no wider than broomstick handles.

I shall get there, vowed Jessamy.

Jessamy always did what she set out to do. And besides, if Ginny could crack it . . .

A few rotten fat cells, thought Jessamy, determinedly stuffing the last of the celery into her mouth, aren't going to beat *me*!

Saul's going-away party coincided happily with the end of term, which meant that Jessamy and Karen could stay out late and enjoy themselves without any pangs of conscience. Belinda Tarrant had instructed them, when they were ready to leave, to call a cab from the cab company which she herself always patronised.

'I don't imagine Saul will be in any fit state to drive you home.'

And anyway, thought Jessamy, why should he?

'I just hope you realise,' continued her mum, 'how privileged you are, being asked to go along? Most young dancers would give their right arms for such a chance.'

'I know I'm privileged,' said Jessamy. Ginny and

Lorraine reminded her of it often enough; she didn't need her mum rubbing it in.

She repeated it, sternly, to Karen, as they set off that evening: 'I hope you realise how privileged you are, being asked to come along . . . most young dancers would give their right arms for such a chance.'

Karen looked at her, startled. Her cheeks grew hot and pink.

'Jessamy, are you *sure* Saul said I could come?'

'Of course he did!'

'You didn't push him?'

'Now, I put it to you,' said Jessamy, 'am I a pushing kind of person?'

Karen opened her mouth.

'All right, you don't have to answer that,' said Jessamy. 'But anyway, I didn't push. He said, "Do you and Karen want to come and kiss me goodbye before I go off on tour?" and – '

'He said *that*?'

'What?'

'What you just said!'

'What did I just say?'

'About – ' Karen blushed even pinker – 'about kissing him goodbye.'

'Why?' Jessamy's eyes sparkled naughtily. 'Do you want to kiss him goodbye? He'll let you kiss him goodbye! I'll tell him that's the only reason you've come.'

'Jessamy! No!' A note of panic entered Karen's voice. 'Don't! Please!'

'Well, then, be properly grateful.'

'I am! You know I am!'

'How do I know? You haven't gone down on your knees. You haven't told me how wonderful I am. You –'

'*Jessamy*!'

'Oh, for goodness' sake!' Jessamy took one look at Karen's distraught face and relented. 'I was only *joking*. You really must learn,' she scolded, 'not to take everything seriously.'

'It's difficult,' pleaded Karen, 'when things are so important –'

'I know.' Jessamy nodded; wise and benevolent. 'You get all worked up. But never mind,' she said, 'you'll grow out of it.'

Half the Company was at Saul's party. Jessamy wasn't in the least bit shy, in fact she didn't know the meaning of the word, but even Jessamy had learnt when to keep a low profile. Being little sister to the Company's leading male dancer didn't mean you could go throwing your weight around and showing off. She smiled and said hallo to people when they noticed her, but she knew better than to push herself forward in such exalted company.

For the most part she stayed in the corner with Karen, drinking soft drinks and whispering comments.

'Look! There's Gemma.' Gemma Dugard, one of the younger dancers. 'Doesn't she look super?'

'Yes, and look, there's Sandro!' Karen poked slyly at Jessamy as Alessandro Corelli strolled in, but Jessamy had grown out of her schoolgirl passion for Sandro ages ago. She could gaze upon him quite calmly, nowadays. In any case, she had never aban-

28

doned herself as wholeheartedly to hero-worship as Karen. It would be highly inconvenient and embarrassing, if you asked Jessamy, to live permanently in a state where you fired up as pink as a peony every time the beloved object came into view.

'There's Colleen.' She nudged at Karen. 'Over there, with Saul.'

Karen looked, and sighed. 'She's so beautiful!'

It was true, Colleen was beautiful, with her abundant brown hair and eyes as blue as sapphires – and not in the least pumpkin-shaped. Just shapely. A dancer with a figure. Dad must be mad if he preferred broom handles. And of course Saul was just being horrid when he complained that lifting Colleen was like lifting a sack of potatoes. Saul and Colleen didn't get on terribly well in spite of often dancing together. Both too much like prima donnas, thought Jessamy, watching as they ritually flung their arms round each other and exchanged kisses.

'It doesn't mean anything,' she whispered comfortingly to Karen. 'It's just what they do.'

'Yes, I know,' said Karen.

'It's what theatricals always do.'

'Yes, I know.' Karen brightened. 'There's Ken!'

'Oh, yes.' Jessamy waved. It seemed permissible to attract Ken's attention. He wasn't a member of the Company, he was an artist, of the drawing and painting kind; and although slowly making a name for himself he hadn't yet achieved Saul's heady pinnacle of fame, so that no one could accuse her of pushing herself forward. After all, if you went to a party you had to talk to *someone*.

29

On and off, they talked to Ken for the rest of the evening. He had once painted a portrait of Karen, so that she knew him quite well and wasn't tongue-tied. Jessamy was even able to leave her with him occasionally and make little forays across the room to fetch another drink or some food and say hallo to people as she went – but never to stay and bore them. She was mature enough to know that when someone like Piet van den Berg or Mark Allmond said 'Hi, Jessamy! How are you?' they were only being polite; they didn't really want to hear all about her battles fighting flab.

After they had been there a couple of hours, Saul detached himself from a little group of people whom Jessamy didn't know and wandered over to exchange a few words. (She could feel Karen glowing like a beacon at her side.)

'Enjoying yourselves?'

Jessamy nodded, happily.

'Not getting drunk, are you?'

'On orange juice?' said Jessamy.

'So long as that's what it is.' Saul sniffed at her glass. 'OK! Just checking. You might have slipped a gin in there while my back was turned.'

'Is there some?' Jessamy looked round, hopefully.

'Not for the likes of you! Mum would never for-give me.'

'I suppose not.' Jessamy remembered her manners. 'This is a very nice party,' she said. 'I feel very privi-leged to have been invited.'

There was a pause.

'Come again?' said Saul.

'Very privileged,' said Jessamy, 'to have been invited.'

'Ye-e-e-es ... good! So what's the catch?'

'What catch?'

'There was a distinct *but* in your voice.'

'Oh! Well, it's just that I hate it when the Company's not in London.'

'We're only away for three months!'

'Yes, but it leaves a great gap in my life ... is Ken going with you?'

'No, unfortunately he can't.'

Ken at that moment was mooching about in the middle of the room with Karen. It couldn't properly be called dancing; there wasn't enough space. But lots of other couples were mooching and it was nice of Ken, thought Jessamy, to put himself out. He wasn't really a mooching sort of person.

'Won't you miss him?' said Jessamy.

'I expect so, but that's the way it goes ... he has his own work to get on with.'

'Yes.' Jessamy sighed. 'It's so difficult,' she said, 'trying to have relationships with people outside the ballet.'

'That sounds very heartfelt! Do I take it you speak from experience?'

'There just aren't enough boys to go round,' said Jessamy. 'And half the ones there are, aren't interested.'

'It's a tough life,' said Saul.

'Well, it is. I hope you'll be faithful while you're away. Ken is so *nice*,' said Jessamy. 'He's far too nice

31

for someone like you. And I know what happens when people go on tour.'

'What?' Saul leaned towards her. 'Tell me!'

'They throw caution to the winds,' said Jessamy, 'and have affairs all over the place. Specially when they're leading dancers and can take their pick. But *I* think,' said Jessamy, 'that it ought to be resisted.'

'Oh, you do, do you?'

'Yes, I do,' said Jessamy.

'Little sister – ' Saul pressed the tip of his finger against her nose – 'watch it! I didn't invite you here to be lectured.'

'I know, and I do feel *very* privileged,' said Jessamy.

'I'm sure! Just stop trying to be humble, it doesn't suit you.'

'But three months,' groaned Jessamy. 'Three months without any ballet . . . it's a lifetime!'

'It's all right, there's no need to panic. You can still come along and have your fix. The theatre's not going to be empty, a Spanish dance troupe's coming in.'

'Really?' Jessamy perked up. That wouldn't be so bad! 'Which one?'

'Carlos Miguel y sus Compañeros.'

Saul drew himself up, hands above his head, back arched. He did a little drum roll with his feet. Jessamy promptly did the same. Finger snapping, heels tapping, they circled each other.

'Olé!' cried Saul.

'Olé!' echoed Jessamy.

She wondered if the day would ever come when

32

she would dance with Saul professionally. Already she could imagine the reviews ... *Saul Hart, premier danseur of City Ballet, last night partnered his younger sister, Jessamy Hart, on her debut as Princess Aurora – not* shaped like a pumpkin. Those hips were going to go!

'Ken's hoping to get backstage and make some sketches.' Saul gave a final stamp. 'So I expect, if you wanted, you could go along with him.'

'Keep an eye on him for you,' agreed Jessamy. 'Spanish dancers are v-e-r-y sexy!'

She leapt away, laughing, as Saul took a swipe at her.

On their way out of the building at midnight, escorted by Saul, they bumped into an elderly grey-haired man, extremely dapper, with a carnation in his buttonhole. Jessamy recognised him at once as Eric Lauder, the ballet critic.

'What's this?' he cried. 'Beating a hasty retreat from your own party? I was just about to make my entrance!' And then he caught sight of Jessamy and said, 'Ah, no! I see. Sending Cinderella home in her coach and four. And how is Cinderella?'

'Very well, thank you,' said Jessamy. You always had to be extra polite to critics.

'And who is this?' He peered down by the light of the street lamp at Karen. 'The face seems familiar ... have we met before? Don't tell me, it will come ... I remember!' He straightened up, pleased with himself. 'The young lady with the good line.' There and then on the pavement, quite unabashed, he sketched an *arabesque*. 'You see? The old elephant never forgets!'

Eric Lauder disappeared, chuckling, into the entrance of the flats.

'See you at the party, dear boy!'

'And what,' demanded Saul, 'was all that about?'

Karen, needless to say, had been rendered speechless. It was left to Jessamy to explain.

'He once caught her *dancing* in the foyer.'

'Dancing in the foyer?'

'At the Fountain.' The Fountain was the Company's theatre. Jessamy and Karen had been to the ballet and Jessamy, afterwards, had gone backstage to see Saul. Karen had been too shy – but not too shy to stand in the middle of the foyer making an exhibition of herself. 'Sticking her leg in the air in front of all those people,' grumbled Jessamy. 'So *vulgar*.'

But the great Eric Lauder had noticed her – and, what was more, remembered. Saul pursed his lips in a silent whistle.

'Well, well! Fame and fortune beckon!'

He bent and kissed Jessamy, then turned and lightly kissed Karen, as well.

'There are times when it obviously pays to be just a little bit vulgar!'

Except that Karen wasn't as a rule, thought Jessamy. She was normally such a timid little creep mouse thing. Extraordinary that on the one occasion when she forgot herself and did something which even brash brazen Jessamy would hesitate to do, she was lucky enough to catch the eye of perhaps the

34

most influential ballet critic in town. Singled out for stardom, thought Jessamy; and wondered why it was she didn't feel more jealous.

'In you get!' Saul was holding open the door of the cab. 'Thank you for coming to say goodbye – and yes! You can keep an eye on Ken for me. As you say, Spanish dancers have *mucho atracción* . . . v-e-r-y sexy!'

Saul went bounding back indoors, to catch up with the party. The cab bore Karen and Jessamy off into the night. After a few minutes, when she had recovered enough to speak, Karen said, 'What did he mean?'

'Saul? About Eric Lauder?'

'No, about looking after Ken.'

'Keeping an eye on him. It was just a joke, really. There's this Spanish dance company coming in, and Ken wants to go backstage and do some sketching. Saul said if we wanted we could probably go with him. I should think we *would* want,' said Jessamy, 'wouldn't you?'

'Mm. I suppose so.' Karen didn't sound desperately enthusiastic. 'It won't be the same as the ballet.'

'No, but it'll still be dancing. One oughtn't to be narrow-minded,' said Jessamy.

'I'm not being narrow-minded. I just said it wouldn't be the same.'

'What you mean is, Saul won't be there!'

Did Karen really think that Jessamy didn't see her put up a hand and touch her cheek where he had kissed her? Pathetic! Oh, pathetic!

3

'I *am* getting fat,' said Jessamy. 'Look!' She grimaced at herself in the studio mirror. 'Look at this!' She pinched at her thigh. 'Fat! Fat! Fat! *Ugh*! It's horrible!'

'I *know*,' said Karen. 'I'm getting fat, too!' She ranged herself alongside Jessamy, a skinny wraith in a black leotard. 'I can squeeze bits of myself between my fingers!'

She was only saying it to make Jessamy feel better. Karen's thighs didn't wobble when she slapped them. *Her* hips didn't balloon out like a great quivering hovercraft.

'I'm really going to start watching what I eat,' said Karen.

All that meant was that she was going to be tactful and not cram bars of chocolate into her mouth in front of Jessamy.

They stood, side by side, in front of the mirror, one skinny blond wraith and one strapping (there was no other word for it, thought Jessamy) one strapping rosy-cheeked *wench*. She was starting to look like an all-in wrestler.

'Watching what you eat isn't the solution.' Moodily, she hoicked up a leg and plonked it down on the barre. It was the first week of the Easter holidays

36

and they were in Belinda Tarrant's studio. Mum had said that provided they were prepared to get up early, before she had any pupils booked, they could put themselves through daily class.

'It's not just food; it's metabolism. Some people don't burn off the calories as quickly as others.'

'I don't think I burn off calories.' Karen said it earnestly. 'Do you know, I weigh more at night than I do in the morning?'

Jessamy never dared weigh herself at night. She flexed her leg, the one that was resting on the barre, and bent over until her head touched her knee. Susan and Sheela had always been impressed when Jessamy did things like that, casually, without even thinking, but there wasn't anything particularly clever about it. Anyone could do it, thought Jessamy, if they started young enough and were prepared to dedicate themselves to daily practice. The pursuit of the unnatural was what the Bottler called it. The Bottler was Jack's husband. He always maintained that ballet was full of tortured cripples trying to force twisted limbs into new and ever more grotesque deformities.

It had to be said, thought Jessamy, bending backwards from the barre, that there was some truth in it. Nature had certainly never intended hips, for instance, to rotate in their sockets and make legs turn out at an angle of ninety degrees – which was why ballet dancers tended to waddle like ducks when they walked. Thank goodness Jessamy had never had any problems with turn-out! Mum had once had a pupil who was really promising but had had no turn-out at all. In the end she had gone to a school of contemporary dance and joined a modern company, where turn-out wasn't quite so important. Jessamy occasionally saw her name mentioned in reviews. She was doing very well but Mum never counted her as one of her successes.

Jessamy wondered if she herself could be happy doing modern dance. If the unthinkable were to happen and Madam threw her out . . .

But Madam wasn't going to throw her out! The unthinkable was unthinkable.

'I have decided,' announced Jessamy, straightening up, 'that starving oneself is not the answer.' She didn't intend to lose control and guzzle chips and crisps and chocolate, but you couldn't exist indefinitely on a diet of raw carrots and celery. 'I'm going to be careful – '

'Yes!' Karen nodded, eagerly. She seemed relieved: Jessamy was such an extremist. 'That's how Ginny's managed to keep at the right weight.'

Jessamy didn't wish to hear about Ginny, just at this moment. Jessamy still had a long way to go.

'So what I have decided,' she said, 'is that I am not *only* going to do class every day, I am going jogging, as well. I thought,' she added carelessly, 'that maybe you ought to come with me to make sure that I do it.'

'You will, if you've made up your mind,' said Karen.

'Yes, but I shall get bored all by myself. It would be much more fun,' urged Jessamy, 'if we did it together.'

Karen hesitated.

'When are you thinking of going?'

'Right away! Immediately!'

'What, after class?'

'While I'm still in the mood.'

'I can do it with you this week,' said Karen, 'but I won't have time after that. I've got this holiday job.'

'Really?' Jessamy looked at Karen in surprise. It was the first she had heard about any holiday job. Why hadn't Karen told her before? She and Jessamy always told each other everything. 'Doing what?'

'Local supermarket.' Karen crinkled her nose. 'Shelf-filling and sticking on prices and stuff.'

'Ugh! How boring!' The words had rushed out before Jessamy could stop them.

Karen blushed – and Jessamy did just a little bit, too. What an awful thing to say! She knew perfectly well that Karen's gran didn't have much money.

'I'm not really looking forward to it,' said Karen, 'but other people do it and I can't let Gran go on paying for me all the time.'

'Is it every day? For the whole holidays?'

'Mm. And I have to be there really early.'

Jessamy pulled a face. Her immediate selfish thought was, what am I going to do without Karen? Up until now, she and Karen had been inseparable in school holidays. How was Jessamy going to fill her time? Even Susan and Sheela had been talking of doing some holiday work.

'P'raps I ought to get a job, too,' said Jessamy.

'Not if you don't have to.'

'But it makes me feel lazy!' Lazy and privileged. 'Don't you think I ought?'

Karen considered the matter, seriously.

'I suppose you could, but for you it would just be extra pocket money, and you don't really need extra pocket money, do you?'

'Not really,' admitted Jessamy. Mum and Dad were very generous. Jessamy was always allowed to take cabs and charge them to her mum's account, and for clothes she even had an account of her own. Perhaps it would actually be rather greedy to go out and earn more. It might mean taking a job away from someone like Karen, who was doing it because she really had to.

Relieved, Jessamy said, 'All right, I won't get a job. I'll concentrate on doing work-outs and going jogging.'

'Yes, because I expect you're right, and it will be boring. At least, I expect it would to you.'

'Oh, I don't know,' said Jessamy, eager now to be encouraging. 'You'll get to meet people, and there'll be all the customers to talk to ... they'll probably keep asking you things, like "Excuse me, where's the cat food?" and "What's happened to that special offer that you had?" I should think,' said Jessamy, 'it might actually be quite interesting.'

She knew as soon as she had said it that meeting people and talking to customers were the very things that Karen was dreading. She wouldn't mind the boredom because unlike Jessamy, whose boredom threshold was uncomfortably low, Karen was a natural-born daydreamer. She could quite easily keep herself amused from morning till night by dancing her favourite roles in her head, or making up ballets to her favourite music. But when you were shy, going into new situations could be terrifying.

It would probably, thought Jessamy, do Karen good to have a holiday job. It was time she branched out on her own, without always having Jessamy at her side to bolster her courage. She couldn't really say as much to Karen, or not in so many words, but at least it took the edge off her own guilty conscience. She could spend the Easter break being privileged and losing weight without having to worry.

'Whichever way you look at it,' she said, 'it will be a new experience. Dancers don't have nearly enough new experiences if you ask me. We just stick inside our own little cocoons and never know what's going on in the rest of the world.'

She guessed, from her expression, that Karen would be perfectly happy to go on sticking inside her own little cocoon.

'I wouldn't be doing it – ' Karen sank down into a *plié* – 'if it weren't for feeling so terrible about always having to ask Gran to pay for everything.'

'Well, you won't have to ask her to pay for your ticket on Saturday, at any rate. That's Saul's treat.'

Saul had bought them two tickets for the Spanish ballet. He must have done it at the last minute, for they had arrived by post the day after the Company had flown off to Europe, together with a note scrawled in Saul's execrable handwriting: *A mi hermana, de su hermano. Don't forget your promise!*

'What promise?' had said Karen, after they had

41

looked up the words *hermana* and *hermano* in a Spanish dictionary and discovered that they meant sister and brother.

'To keep an eye on Ken,' Jessamy had said, and giggled. 'Make sure the sexy Spanish dancers don't get him!'

'Does he know you're going to keep an eye on him?' Karen said it very solemnly. She didn't always understand about jokes.

'I shall tell him!' said Jessamy.

Belinda Tarrant tended to be a bit snooty about Spanish dancing. No discipline, she said; no history. Classical ballet went back centuries! Spanish dancing (sniff) was really no more than glorified tap.

'I disagree,' said Jessamy's dad. (He and Jessamy's mum almost always disagreed, purely as a matter of principle.) 'I disagree entirely! The best exponents have brought it to a form of high art.'

'Art!' Jessamy's mum gave a little tinkle of laughter. 'Just stamp stamp stamp, snap snap snap.' She demonstrated, in the middle of the kitchen. 'Terribly bad for the spine.'

'There are those,' retorted Jessamy's dad, 'who would say that classical ballet is terribly bad for the joints.'

'Not if people are trained properly.'

'Which they frequently aren't.'

'That's hardly the fault of the ballet! What I cannot stand,' said Jessamy's mum, 'is all that dreadful moaning and wailing that goes on.'

'What moaning and wailing?' said Jessamy.

'The so-called singing.'

'Flamenco,' said Jessamy's dad.

'Whatever it is. They always sound as if they're in their death throes. I can never understand why they don't lose their voices – or maybe they have, poor things.'

'Flamenco,' said Jessamy's dad, 'is a highly stylised form of vocal expression.'

Belinda Tarrant swept on, ignoring him. 'And all those fearsome grim-faced men twanging away in the background on their guitars . . . why can't they ever smile, for goodness' sake?'

'Flamenco is not a smiling matter. You won't get any *Fille Mal Gardées* in flamenco.'

La Fille Mal Gardée was number one on Ben Hart's list of most hated ballets. Jessamy was never quite sure what he had against it, though it was true that her dad tended to favour ballets which had messages rather than ballets that were just fun. If ever Saul and Jacquetta had wanted to annoy him, in the days before Jack was married and Saul still lived at home, they had gone into their clog dance routine. It had never failed to produce a tirade.

'Candyfloss! Marshmallow! Twee! Trite! Trivial!'

Needless to say, Mum always rose up in its defence.

There were times when Jessamy sided with her dad, times when she sided with her mum. On this occasion, she couldn't quite make up her mind.

'Do you really think Spanish dancing is a form of high art?' she said, when she and her dad were alone together.

'Most certainly it is!'

'But it hasn't any history,' said Jessamy.

'Rubbish! It's full of history. Goes back centuries.'

'But Mum s – '

'My dear girl, you don't necessarily want to believe everything your mother says. She argues for the sake of arguing! The traditional dances of Spain have been around for far longer than classical ballet. As for all that nonsense about flamenco . . . in southern Spain flamenco is a way of life. To say it's nothing but wailing and moaning is simply to betray one's ignorance – unless, of course, one has had the misfortune to sit through a bad performance. There are second-rate Spanish dancers just as there are second-rate anything else.'

'Do you think that Carlos Miguel will be second rate?'

'I shouldn't imagine so, but go along and see,' was Ben Hart's advice.

'But how will I know?' worried Jessamy.

'You'll know,' said her dad. 'Or you're no daughter of mine!'

The only Spanish dancing Jessamy could remember seeing was a video brought back from Spain several years ago by Marisol, one of the Harts' au pairs. The video was called *La Noche de Luz*. She dug it out and she and Karen sat down together one evening to watch. At the end, there was a long silence; then Jessamy removed the video and put it back in its case.

'It was – quite fun,' said Karen.

'Mm.' Jessamy nodded. 'I liked the costumes.'

44

'The costumes were *beautiful*.'

They didn't mention it again until Saturday evening, when they stood waiting together on the platform at Chiswick Park for a tube.

'Mum thinks Spanish dancing is nothing but glorified tap,' complained Jessamy.

Karen sighed, regretfully. 'Yes,' she said.

She said it without thinking. Her mind at that moment was dwelling less on the evening's entertainment than on the horrors to come on Monday morning when she had to start work at the supermarket.

'What do you mean, *yes*?'

'Well. I – ' Karen floundered. 'I mean, I – I agree with her, really. I suppose.'

She gave a little apologetic smile as she said it. It had, after all, been extremely generous of Saul to buy them tickets. It was very ungrateful of her to say that she thought Spanish dancing was only glorified tap, even if it had been Jessamy's mum who had said it first.

'What do you actually *know* about it?' demanded Jessamy.

'Well – not very much,' admitted Karen. 'Only what we saw on that video.'

'Forget the video! The video was rubbish.' Lots of head tossing and skirt swishing but nothing that could properly be called dancing. 'Don't worry,' said Jessamy, 'the real thing will be heaps better!'

But she crossed her fingers as she said it.

Ken was waiting for them in the theatre foyer. Unlike Saul, who was quite neat and compact, Ken was long and gangly, with an untidy thatch of sandy-coloured hair and a face like a friendly horse.

'It was ever so nice of Saul to buy tickets for us,' said Karen, anxious to make amends for her earlier ungraciousness.

'Oh! It was all done from ulterior motives,' said Jessamy. 'We're here to keep an eye on Ken and save him from the Spanish dancers. Spanish dancers,' said Jessamy, 'are v-e-r-y sexy!'

Ken grinned.

Karen said, 'They weren't on that video.'

'Don't keep on about the video! This'll be different. Live performances always are.'

Jessamy sounded confident, because she was a confident person, but Marisol's video had certainly been a bad experience. Suppose that *was* all Spanish dancing consisted of? Just a bit of swishing and foot stamping and clacking of castanets? That would mean that Mum was right and Dad was wrong. Suddenly, desperately, she didn't want Dad to be wrong.

While Karen sat prattling to Ken, Jessamy read through her programme. There was a big glossy photograph of Carlos Miguel, hawk-faced, aristocratic, with an aquiline nose, smiling wolfishly beneath a wide-brimmed Spanish hat. There were photographs of individual members of the company – Maria Rojas, Pilar Amaya, Paco Gonzalez, Luis Martín – in various poses (Jessamy studied them, carefully: they all looked to her like trained dancers) and finally a photograph of the entire company in a ballet called *El Amor Brujo*, or *Love, the Magician*, set to music by Manuel de Falla. Surely Mum

46

couldn't dismiss *El Amor Brujo* as glorified tap dancing?

She heard Ken say to Karen, 'I think you'll find there's a bit more to it than that,' and then the house lights dimmed. Jessamy tensed with anticipation. Please let Dad be right!

She knows, as soon as the curtain goes up, that he is. The stage is bare save for a bench and deep crimson drapes at the back. Suddenly the drapes part and three proud men enter, stamping. All are dressed in black, and all seem rather fierce. After a preliminary stamp round the stage they freeze to the spot, clap their hands once very loudly and shout, for no apparent reason, 'Olé!'

Three more men enter, carrying guitars. They are also dressed in black and also rather fierce. They slink across the stage, lower themselves in unison to the bench, stare forbiddingly for a few seconds into the auditorium then bend with deep and reverential severity over their guitars.

Yet another black-clad man appears, grim-faced and sombre. It is no laughing matter, this Spanish dance.

The newcomer takes up his stand by the guitarists, sternly clears his throat and twists his neck out of his collar. He opens his mouth and lets out a cry, loud and hoarse, then passes a hand across his throat, the effort appearing to have wearied him. He plants his feet further apart, holds out both arms and tries again. A series of staccato wails fill the theatre. The man is a flamenco singer!

A woman now comes on, wearing a long flounced dress of orange and flame red. She starts to clap her hands to the plangent notes of the three hunched guitarists. A beat, and then the singer throws back his head and emits another harsh, wailing cry.

The three sombre figures, poised like statues, rouse themselves to give a few brief, defiant stamps before falling back rigidly into their aloof and angular positions as a raving madman bursts from the wings and skids across the stage on one knee. It is Carlos Miguel! He is wearing his broad-brimmed hat, white shirt with short red jacket, bold-patterned neckerchief and high-waisted black trousers. Jessamy recognises him from the glossy photograph.

He raises himself to his full height and inclines his head, gravely, in acknowledgement of the rapturous applause that has greeted his arrival. The three proud men at the back studiously ignore him. They have their noses in the air, standing still as stone.

The singer lets out another of his harsh cries and Carlos Miguel begins to dance, a strange, stern kind of dancing, jaw set, hands clutching the bottom edges of his jacket, feet tapping in slow rhythm. The woman joins him, in her orange-flame dress. They circle each other as the singer wails his incomprehensible song. The only words of the song that Jessamy can catch are 'Ay! Ay!' And even then, perhaps, he is just clearing his throat.

The pace increases as the two dancers twirl and stamp. The woman crouches and crosses the stage bent almost double. Carlos Miguel crashes down first on one knee, then on the other. (Jessamy winces: it

48

looks painful.) He leaps up and pursues the woman across the stage in a series of bone-shaking convulsions. Palms are cracking, fingers snap. The rhythm of the three hunched men grows in intensity, the singer looks near to bursting a blood vessel, his guttural cries rising hoarsely above the sounds of the guitars.

Carlos Miguel winds his body into an impossible spiral, stamping and spinning at the same time. The woman, meanwhile (she is Pilar Amaya, Jessamy discovers afterwards from the programme), has her arms raised above and just slightly behind her head, her back arched, her fingers splayed. Expertly, with a barely perceptible flick of the foot, she kicks the train of her dress out of harm's way.

What it all means, Jessamy cannot say. She only knows that it makes the blood go pulsing through her veins, makes her feet itch and tingle with the desire to join in.

'Olé!' she cries, along with one of the guitarists, as Carlos Miguel, with a final flourish, whips off his scarf, loops it about Pilar Amaya's neck and triumphantly bears her off, she with her hands on her hips, he waving his hat in the air in symbol, Jessamy supposes, of victory.

The audience clap themselves into a near frenzy, and Jessamy claps with them. So does Karen, though not quite as enthusiastically as Jessamy. Surely she cannot have failed to be impressed?

The next piece before the interval is more classical, a 'Sonata' to music by Granados. It is set, Jessamy remembers from her programme, in sixteenth-century Spain, with all the men wearing doublet and hose and small ruffs, and the women in silk dresses with wide panniered skirts and laced bodices. All the dancers are in ballet shoes, and some of the women actually go on point. Jessamy hadn't realised that this ever happened in Spanish dancing. She enjoys the piece, but it doesn't thrill her as the first, flamenco, number did. She wants more of the blood and sinew! This is too polite, though she likes it when the castanets chatter and purr. (She wonders if it is easy to play the castanets and whether she should buy herself a pair.)

In the interval, Karen admits to being pleasantly surprised, though she stops short of actually waxing delirious. Ken, on the other hand, is desperate to start making his sketches. He is going to attend rehearsals next week and maybe, if the Company grow to accept him, they will let him go backstage.

During the second half there is a number called *Soleares* (the first one was *Tanguillos*) with Paco Gonzalez and Luis Martín, Maria Rojas and two other women whose names Jessamy can't remember. This is flamenco again, and Jessamy loves it. Maria Rojas, she thinks, is very beautiful, with her deep red hair and full, pouting lips; and one of the men – she can't be sure whether it's Paco Gonzalez or Luis Martín – has the same magnetic good looks as Carlos Miguel: the same thick, glossy black hair, the same aquiline nose and dark, brooding features. This is what Jessamy expects a flamenco dancer to be!

After the *Soleares* comes a gentler number, *Danse Basque*, in which the whole Company perform. They

50

are all dressed in colourful Basque costumes, including berets, long white skirts and scarlet jackets for the women, scarlet jackets and short black trousers for the men, and everyone is wearing soft boots which make no sound as they pad about the stage. At one point two of the girls take it in turns to jump on and off an upturned tumbler placed in front of the footlights. Jessamy cannot imagine what the significance of this is, perhaps it is only fun, but she can't wait to try it! One of the boys then cheekily performs the same feat. 'See?' he seems to be saying. 'It's not so clever! Anyone can do it' – and the audience laugh and applaud. It's the boy with the brooding features who looks like Carlos Miguel.

This boy appears in the next number, too – something called *Caña*, which to Jessamy's delight turns out to be yet more flamenco. Flamenco, she has decided, is what she loves best of all.

The boy, whoever he is – either Paco Gonzalez or Luis Martín, she will look at her programme later, for the moment she cannot take her eyes off the stage – is extremely good. Jessamy has a dancer's eye that tells her Belinda Tarrant is quite wrong. There *is* a discipline in Spanish dancing. Possibly, she suspects, there is more improvisation than actual set steps (which wouldn't please her mum) but this boy has been trained.

For *Caña* he wears a grey jacket and trousers. The jacket is decorated with three black tassels at either side. His waistcoat is a brilliant crimson, embroidered in silver with some kind of flower pattern.

Walking slowly, deliberately, one arm extended

above his head, one held out before him, he snaps his fingers in time to the music. Now he points the rhythm with quick jabs of the toe, spins in a tight circle, then moves off across the stage with a kind of swaying walk – arrogant, very sure of himself – both arms raised above his head, fingers still snapping.

He stops. His head flings back and he begins a pulsating drumming with the feet, punctuated from time to time with vicious stabs of heel and toe.

Jessamy's blood thrills. This is what she had dreamed of! This was everything she had thought Spanish dancing should be! Marisol's tape was not representative. It was cheap stuff, such as tourists might see. Such as you might find in a night club. This was the real thing!

The last number of the evening is a whirling *Sevillanas* for the full company. A spectacle, thinks Jessamy, to send people away happy. She would have preferred more flamenco, but maybe not everyone shares her tastes. Most people probably like something a bit less austere (audiences always prefer *La Fille Mal Gardée* to any of her dad's abstract creations).

But Ben Hart was right. Spanish dancing is an art form! And Jessamy is her dad's daughter: she can tell a good performance when she sees one. Carlos Miguel and his Company are brilliant!

'That was just so incredible!' declared Jessamy, when Ken had waved them goodbye and seen them safely off in their cab. 'The way they use their whole body – the way they express themselves! It couldn't be more different from the ballet! It makes ballet seem almost – ' she searched for the word – 'almost like – like *tinsel*. Like – froth! As if it doesn't have any substance. This is all earthy, and bloody, and – and primitive!'

Jessamy talked, excitedly and non-stop, all the way to Chiswick. Karen said very little beyond the odd 'Mm' or 'Ah,' but then she was not really given much opportunity. It wasn't until the cab had turned into her road and they were nearly at her gran's house that she said carelessly, 'Maybe we should go again.'

Jessamy was definitely going to go again. 'But I thought you agreed with Mum that it was only glorified tap?'

Karen's cheeks glowed pink in the semi-darkness. *Now* what was she blushing for?

'I might be able to get used to it ... if I saw a bit more of it. And now that I've got a job – ' she threw open the door of the cab – 'I'll be able to afford it!'

4

Stamp, stamp, rattle rattle *click*.

Stamp, turn, stamp stamp *click*.

Jessamy stopped, exasperated. Castanets were not as easy to play as they looked. She had no trouble with the stamping, she was even able to drum her heels quite satisfactorily and could snap her fingers to perfection – and not just the middle one, but the one next to it, as well. It was the castanets which were defeating her. When Carlos Miguel and his company had played them, they had chattered and purred in continuous rhythm. The best that Jessamy could produce was a feeble click, or at the most a clack.

She looked again at the photograph of Pilar Amaya in the programme and studied it carefully. The cord of the castanets was looped over her thumb and she seemed to be using her middle finger to play them. Maybe the secret was to have the loop pulled really tight.

Jessamy pulled the loop really tight and tried again. It was immediately better! At least now you could tell that it was castanets and not just a bit of old ruler being rattled in a jam jar. She had been starting to worry that maybe the castanets she had bought were too cheap, and that you had to have proper professional ones carved out of some special kind of wood if you wanted to make a good sound. Of course, if you were a real Spanish dancer you probably would have special ones, but you didn't start learning the violin on a Stradivarius, reasoned Jessamy, clacking away as fast as she could.

She clacked and stamped for most of the morning, down in the basement kitchen where there was lots of room. Mum was out teaching, Dad was up in Edinburgh, mounting a production for Ballet Roundabout. She wouldn't have dared do it while they were there. Mum would be convinced she was going to cause herself some terrible injury.

'Jessamy, stop! You'll jar your spine!'

She might if the floor were stone, like it was in the pantry and the scullery, but it wasn't, it was wood, because the cellars were below. It was good and springy and quite soft. Jessamy wasn't an idiot. She knew better than to stamp about on concrete, especially in high heels.

Jessamy had bought the high heels when she had bought the castanets. They were the first pair she had ever had, because both Mum and Madam insisted they were bad for you, they said they shortened the Achilles tendon; but it seemed, from watching Carlos Miguel and his company, that you couldn't do flamenco without high heels. All the women had them.

So here was Jessamy, down in the basement, wearing her long skirt and her new forbidden heels, stamping and twirling and clicking her castanets, pretending she was Pilar Amaya, or maybe Maria Rojas with her wine red hair and pouting lips, or maybe just Jessamy Hart, the British-born flamenco dancer hailed all over Spain as *La Inglesa* . . .

She had actually found some guitar music amongst Dad's old tapes, and although it wasn't flamenco, or at least she didn't think it was, it gave her something to dance to. This afternoon she was going to go into town and see if she could find some proper flamenco music.

Stamp, twirl, clickety-clackety-click. She was getting it! She was getting it!

Stamp, twirl –

CRASH.

Ow! Jessamy rubbed ruefully at her ankle. That was another bruise. She kept forgetting to flick the hem of her skirt out of the way as she turned, so that her heels kept catching in it and sending her off balance. That was the second time she had ricocheted into the edge of the table.

This was ridiculous, thought Jessamy, crossly. She was supposed to be a trained dancer! She never had any problem wearing long skirts in ballet, but then she was usually wearing ballet shoes rather than high heels. In the few ballets where heels were required, either the skirts were short or the dances slow and stately. Some of the women in Carlos Miguel's company had worn dresses that were not only long and flouncy, but had trains, as well. Imagine spinning and stamping with a train! Jessamy considered whether to pin a tablecloth to her skirt, but decided against it. Best tackle the basics first.

Stamp, twirl, clickety-clackety-click. *Stamp*, twirl –

Bother! That was the telephone.

Jessamy stamped and clicked her way across the kitchen.

'Hallo?'

'Jessamy?' It was Karen.

'Where are you ringing from?' said Jessamy. 'I thought you were at work.'

'I am, but it's my lunch break.'

'Already? It's only half-past eleven!'

'I know, but some people have to have lunch early.'

'I was going to come in and say hallo to you,' said Jessamy, 'but I thought I wouldn't until you'd had a chance to settle down.'

'Thank you.' Karen actually sounded grateful for Jessamy's thoughtfulness. It wasn't like Jessamy to be thoughtful. 'I didn't ring you yesterday 'cause yesterday was horrible.'

Yesterday had been Karen's first day. While Jessamy had been out buying castanets and high heels, Karen had been stuck in a supermarket learning how to stock shelves and stick on prices. Jessamy felt one of her periodic pangs of conscience.

'Is it getting any better?'

'Mm . . . I suppose so. A little bit.'

'But aren't there lots of you?' said Jessamy.

'There's some people from Upfield.' Upfield was the local comprehensive. 'But they all know each other.'

And Karen, of course, was too shy to go and talk. It wouldn't worry Jessamy, but Karen was what Belinda Tarrant called 'backwards in pushing herself forward'. Fortunately, at ballet school she didn't need to push herself forward because right from the beginning Madam had singled her out.

'Well, it's only for three weeks,' said Jessamy, trying to sound bracing and cheerful. 'It's not as if you're condemned to it for life.'

'Oh, no, I know! And I don't mind so much now that we've got the Spanish dancing to go to.'

'Do you really want to go again?' said Jessamy. She herself had already quite decided on it.

'I think we ought,' said Karen. 'Don't you?'

'*I* think we ought,' said Jessamy.

'So do I. So what I wanted to know –' a note almost of excitement had crept into Karen's voice – 'what I wanted to know was, when shall we go?'

'Soon as you like,' said Jessamy.

'See, I was thinking, I get Wednesday afternoons off, 'cause of having to work Saturdays, so –'

'We could go to the matinée!'

'The only thing is,' said Karen, 'I don't get paid till Saturday and I don't want to have to ask Gran if she can lend me anything.'

'That's all right,' said Jessamy. 'I'll pay and you can pay me back later.'

'You won't get expensive seats, will you?' Karen said it anxiously. Jessamy sometimes forgot that not everyone was as privileged as she was.

'Gallery slips,' promised Jessamy; and 'Gallery slips,' she confirmed, when she rang Karen back after supper.

The gallery slips were where the students always went, on their cheap-rate tickets. They were not only high up in the gods but tucked away down the side, which meant that a part of the stage was cut off and all the dancers looked like matchsticks.

'But it's all right,' said Jessamy, 'we can borrow Mum's opera glasses. They'll be really good for solo numbers. How did things go this afternoon?'

'It's still horrible,' said Karen, 'but I can put up with it if it's going to pay for tickets.'

'Well, this is it,' said Jessamy. 'At least it means you've got something to look forward to.'

Jessamy spent the rest of the evening in her bedroom, jumping on and off her toothmug, trying to balance on the rim the way the girls had done in the Basque ballet. She found that if she wore her bedroom slippers, which were big and flat and fluffy, it was actually quite easy.

The programme for the Wednesday matinée was different from the one they had seen before. Jessamy thought at first that she was going to be disappointed, because there wasn't much flamenco. The afternoon started with scenes from *Carmen*, with Paco Gonzalez and Maria Rojas. It was fun, but it wasn't flamenco; more like ordinary ballet with a Spanish flavour. Jessamy didn't in the least mind letting Karen monopolise the opera glasses. She had a quick look through them, just to remind herself which one Paco Gonzalez was (he was the one with the hawklike features, who resembled Carlos Miguel) and then handed them over.

'Don't you want them back?' whispered Karen; but Jessamy shook her head. She thought that probably Karen preferred the ballet numbers to the flamenco ones. Probably most people did; afternoon programmes always concentrated on the most popular items in a company's repertoire.

After *Carmen* came a solo number by Pilar Amaya wearing high-waisted Spanish trousers, embroidered waistcoat, starched shirt and tasselled boots, everything gleaming white save for the decorations on the waistcoat and the silver tassels on the boots. To the accompaniment of the three hunched guitarists and the hoarse-voiced singer, she stamped and twisted, curled her arms, snapped her fingers, now doubled over as if in pain, now drawn up, proud, straight, stiff, finally making her exit with a series of handclaps – but what handclaps! Handclaps like pistol shots, which echoed round the theatre.

Oh! thought Jessamy, lowering the opera glasses, which she had greedily snatched back from Karen. That is what I want to do!

After the interval there was a comic ballet called *Los Lagarteranos*, where an unsuspecting husband comes across his wife sewing baby clothes. Luis Martín danced the husband, and someone called Isabel Flores the wife. Jessamy and Karen peaceably passed the opera glasses back and forth. Jessamy thought, Dad would probably put this on his hate list with *La Fille Mal Gardée* (twee! trite! trivial!) but predictably it met with rapturous applause. Matinée audiences weren't always the most sophisticated. Some of Dad's best ballets had been greeted with no more than cool politeness at afternoon performances.

The last item on the programme was a *zapateado* for solo dancer. The curtain rose on a stage completely bare save for one lone figure – Paco Gonzalez: Jessamy could recognise him by now – bathed in an amber light.

He stood erect, one hand grasping the edge of his jacket, the other resting on his thigh. After a few seconds, still grasping his jacket with one hand, he let the other go twisting upwards, snakelike, to a position above his head, while at the same time his feet, almost soundlessly at first, but growing in intensity, began a brisk thrumming, his body swaying rhythmically.

Jessamy's blood pounded in her veins. Her toes curled up inside her shoes. Eyes riveted to the stage, she heard, rather than actually saw, the rapid patter of his feet, heels drumming like castanets upon the floor.

Every now and again a foot would whip out and back. The dancer would writhe and spiral, jerk his head, jut his chin, holding the pose, arrogance personified.

Now he was travelling in a circle, picking up first one foot then the other, lightly brushing his calves with either palm. Now in a straight line, back and forth, propelling himself along it in a series of convulsions. Now with his hands he beat a frenzied tattoo on both thighs, all the time his heels keeping up their steady drumbeat, rat-a-tat-a-tat!

Then suddenly, with alternate feet, arms held high, nostrils dilated, he struck three thudding hammer blows, *smash*, *smash*, *smash*, one after another, hard into the floor.

Silence.

Jessamy, never taking her eyes off the stage, reached out for the opera glasses – but Karen, too, was transfixed. The opera glasses remained firmly clamped to her eyes. Jessamy shot her a venomous sideways glance. Whose opera glasses were they? How selfish! What did Karen want them for? This was the real thing, not watered-down ballet!

She swivelled her eyes back to the front. Slowly and deliberately, arms held out from his body, fingers snapping, the dancer was moving to a position centre stage. Sideways on to the audience, he brought his heels together, and clutching both edges of his jacket as if for dear life began again on his drumming; loud at first, louder and ever louder, faster, ever faster, then gradually diminishing, winding down, dying away, until it could scarcely be heard; until it was just a muttering, just a murmur, just a faint feathering of feet brushing the floor, and not a soul moving, nor even breathing, for fear of missing the final whisper of sound.

The end, when it came, came abruptly. His legs grew taut, the feet stilled. Head flung back he stood there, one hand clutching his jacket, the other gripping his thigh: the same pose with which he had begun.

A second for the audience to recover themselves – for the ordeal had been theirs almost as much as the dancer's – and then the applause roared forth, a solid wall of sound, of hand against hand.

'That,' hissed Jessamy, 'was utterly incredible.' Just let Mum try another of her jibes about glorified tap! 'Didn't you think so?' She turned, almost aggressively on Karen. 'Didn't you think that was incredible?'

'Yes. Yes, it was! Jessamy –' Karen caught urgently at Jessamy's arm. 'Let's go and wait at the stage door!'

'You want to go and wait at the stage door?' Jessamy stared at her, in amazement. That didn't sound like shy Karen!

It didn't sound like a person who thought that Spanish dancing was nothing more than glorified tap, either; but after such a display, who could ever think so? Tap dancing and Paco Gonzalez' *zapateado*? There was no comparison!

'Jessamy, please!' Karen was still clutching, fervently, at Jessamy's arm.

'I don't mind,' said Jessamy. 'But I'll have Mum's opera glasses back!'

'Sorry, I hogged them.' Karen handed them over, shamefaced. 'You should have asked.'

'I did,' said Jessamy. 'You didn't hear. But I forgive you.'

She would forgive Karen anything for agreeing with her that on this occasion Dad had been right and Mum wrong. She couldn't have said why, but it suddenly seemed desperately important that Karen should agree with her.

'Come on, then!' She slipped the opera glasses into her bag. 'If we're going.'

The curtain had just swung up for a second curtain call and Karen was staring mesmerised at the stage. Jessamy prodded her.

'Do you want to or not?'

'Yes!'

'Well, come on, then!'

With evident difficulty Karen tore herself away and together they clattered down the gallery stairs, ahead of the crowd. Jessamy knew from experience, from all those times in the past when she had waited faithfully for autographs outside this very same theatre – outside the Coliseum, outside the Royal Opera House, outside every theatre in London that had ever given house room to a ballet company – that you needed to stake your claim early if you were to stand any chance of a good position. No sense being squashed up at the back and unable to see.

'Have you got your autograph book?' Jessamy giggled. She hadn't waited for an autograph since her first year at ballet school!

'I don't want an autograph, I just want – '

'What?'

A rosy glow spread itself across Karen's cheeks. 'I just want to stand and watch.'

'Why? Are you too scared?' Jessamy giggled again. She was enjoying this! 'I'll get one for you. Which one do you want?'

'I don't want any one! Jessamy, don't!'

'Well, but we can't just stand here gawping . . . they *expect* people to want their autographs. Saul would be mortally offended if his fans didn't shove their autograph books at him.'

'But I haven't got an autograph book!'

Jessamy opened her bag and pulled out her pocket diary. 'This'll do.'

'Oh, Jessamy!' wailed Karen. 'It's so embarrassing!'

'So you want us to go home?'

'No, I just want to be a – a fly on the wall!'

'I don't,' said Jessamy. Jessamy was not by nature a spectator. 'Now that I'm here, I'm going to get an autograph.'

By the time the stage door opened and the artists began to come out, a sizeable crowd had gathered, with Jessamy right at the front and Karen taking shelter behind her.

Members of the *corps de ballet* (were they called that in Spanish dancing, wondered Jessamy?) were the first to emerge. Jessamy let the crowd surge round them. She was after bigger fish than that! The daughter of Ben Hart and Belinda Tarrant didn't stoop to asking mere members of the *corps* for their autographs.

Luis Martín appeared looking disappointingly dim and ordinary, and not at all Spanish, without all the trappings of embroidered waistcoats and frilled shirts. Jessamy let him go; there were enough others waiting to besiege him. Various minor soloists followed, then Maria Rojas came out, as glamorous off stage as on. This was more like it! Boldly, Jessamy thrust her way up to her, cavalierly elbowing people out of the way.

'Excuse me, Miss Rojas! Could I have your autograph?'

Karen waited, in agony. Why, oh why, couldn't Jessamy ever be content to take a back seat? All Karen wanted was to stand quite quietly and look!

Jessamy came bouncing triumphantly back, waving her diary.

'See?' She showed Karen an illegible scrawl all across Wednesday 6 April. 'I got one! We can go now.'

'Oh, Jessamy, not yet! Let's wait a bit longer.'

'But I shouldn't think anyone else is going to come out. People don't always, between shows.'

Karen's face fell.

'Well, I suppose we can wait if you like, but – '

Jessamy broke off as the crowd made a little surge forward. The stage door had half opened and Paco Gonzalez could be glimpsed, talking to Pete, the stage doorkeeper. He was barefooted, with a towel about his shoulders. Jessamy turned to Karen.

'I don't think he's actually going to come out.'

'No.' Karen spoke the word in a hushed whisper. Her cheeks were glowing like twin beacons. Jessamy studied her a moment. Aha! she thought. So that was it! A wicked glint appeared in her eye.

'Shall I go and ask *him* for his autograph?'

'Oh, Jessamy . . . no!'

'I think I will,' said Jessamy.

Determinedly, Jessamy marched forward. She wasn't scared of stage doors! She had been going in and out of this particular one for most of her life.

'Excuse me.' She didn't quite set foot inside, because they didn't like that. Even Pete wouldn't like it when another company was in residence, even if her parents were Ben Hart and Belinda Tarrant. Jessamy knew when to obey the rules. 'I wonder,' she said, meekly, 'if I could have your autograph?'

Paco Gonzalez turned to look at her. His gaze was, without any doubt, arrogant: piercing black eyes which could frazzle you, thought Jessamy, if you were a timid soul like Karen. Fortunately, Jessamy wasn't.

'*Por favor?*' she said. '*Señor?*'

He laughed at that, and took the diary from her, and the pen that she was holding out.

'*Su nombre?*'

Your name. Thank goodness for Marisol!

'Karen,' said Jessamy. She said it without so much as a blush. She even spelt it for him.

For Karen, he wrote, in spiky Spanish handwriting. Jessamy beamed.

'*Muchas gracias, señor!*'

'*De nada!*' He flashed her a grin as he handed back her book and pen. He was certainly very good-looking, thought Jessamy, and nowhere near as old as he at first appeared. Maybe no more than seventeen. Imagine being a leading soloist at seventeen! When Saul was seventeen he had still been in the *corps.*

'I thought your zapateado was absolutely brilliant,' said Jessamy, with her usual impulsiveness. Well, and why not? Everyone liked to know that people had enjoyed their performance; it was what it was all about. 'I've never seen anything like it,' she said.

He grinned again, and dipped his head – sleek, black and glossy – in acknowledgement. Pete looked at Jessamy and rounded his mouth into a prune of mock disapproval.

'*Adios!*' cried Jessamy.

She slipped back out, into the crowd. Some of them were looking at her quite crossly – how dared she steal a march on them like that? – others with envy. Jessamy forged her way through them till she reached Karen.

'I got it,' she said.

'Oh, Jessamy!' breathed Karen.

'Might as well go now. Yes?'

Karen nodded. 'What – was he like?' she managed to say, as they left the crowd behind.

'Quite friendly, really.' In spite of looking arrogant.

'*Really*?'

'Well, he didn't bite my head off.'

'Did he – say anything – to you?'

'Mm. Asked me what my name was. So I told him . . . Karen.'

'You told him your name was Karen?'

'Yes.'

'Jessamy!' Karen's eyes grew wide. 'What did you do that for?'

'I was feeling generous,' said Jessamy. 'I'd already got one autograph; I thought you'd like one. Here!' She ripped the page out of her diary. Karen stared at it. *For Karen. Best wishes, Paco Gonzalez.*

'Well, go on!' said Jessamy. 'Take it! It's not contaminated or anything. And after all,' she said, 'it's not much use to me, is it?'

Slowly, Karen shook her head.

'Put it away in a safe place,' said Jessamy, 'and don't lose it.'

'I won't!' said Karen.

They walked on towards the Embankment and the underground.

'Shall we go again on Saturday,' said Jessamy, 'if I

can get tickets? And next Wednesday? Shall we go
again next Wednesday?'

'I think – ' Karen said it simply – 'that we should
go *every single week*, just as often as we can.'

5

Wednesday 6 April
*This afternoon I went with Jessamy to see the Spanish
dancing for the second time. Paco Gonzalez danced
the lead in* Carmen; *he played a bull fighter who is
in love with Carmen. I don't approve of bull fighting
but the costumes they wear are very sexy (Jessamy
was right!!!). They are called 'suits of lights' and are
very tight-fitting and glittery. Carmen was danced by
Maria Rojas who Jessamy thinks is beautiful. I personally think she is attractive but rather fat, but on
the other hand lots of the women in Spanish dancing
are quite plump compared to ballet dancers. Maybe
it doesn't matter so much as there aren't so many lifts,
in fact hardly any at all. I think that Spanish dancing
is more earthbound than ballet. The idea in ballet is
to look weightless as if you could float or fly, but in
Spanish dancing there is a lot of banging and stamping and falling down on your knees, which looks very
painful to me I must say.*

*At the end Paco danced a solo called a 'zapateado'.
(Jessamy pronounces this 'thapatayardo', which I
expect is probably correct since she picked up lots of
bits of Spanish from when Marisol was there. I wish
I could speak Spanish! I think I might get a book out
of the library.)*

The zapateado *was very amazing. There was no music at all, just the tapping of feet, which you might think would get boring but it doesn't in the least. I was watching through Jessamy's mum's opera glasses (which I hogged) and his heels and toes were moving so fast it was almost too fast to see, just a blur. He must have the most incredible muscle control.*

The really best bit came afterwards when we waited at the stage door and saw him standing there talking to the stage doorkeeper with a towel round his neck. Jessamy went and asked him for his autograph and said her name was Karen!!! So now I have a piece of paper with his handwriting on! I have stuck it in my scrap book next to Saul's that Jessamy also got for me. I think she only did it for a joke. I don't think she realises how much it means to me.

We are going to go and watch the Company again on Saturday if Jessamy can get tickets. I am keeping my fingers crossed. If only I had the money I would go every single day!

Thursday 7 April
Hooray! We've got the tickets for Saturday. I'll have to rush like mad and go straight there from the supermarket as they stay open late on Saturdays. I still hate it, work I mean, because everyone else knows each other and nobody speaks to me which I know is my own fault because I am too stupid and shy, but I am marking the days off on the calendar and I don't mind so much now that it has a purpose. (The purpose is going to see the Spanish dancing just as often as I possibly can.)

71

*Gran won't take any money off me. She says she's
managed all right so far and she'll go on managing.
She says I can make it up to her when I'm famous.
Oh, will I ever be! Jessamy will. She is cut out for
fame. But for myself I just cannot imagine it.*

Friday 8 April
*Gran said to me today, 'Goodness me! Going to the
theatre again?' (When I told her about Saturday.) She
wasn't being disapproving, just surprised. She said,
'I'd have thought you'd want to spend your hard-
earned money buying some nice clothes for yourself,
not having a busman's holiday.'*

*A busman's holiday, it seems, is when you do the
same thing on your days off as you do on the days
when you're working. I had to explain to Gran that
it was necessary for dancers to go and watch other
dancers. Fortunately she accepted this before I had a
chance to start blushing!*

Sunday 10 April
Last night we saw El Amor Brujo *(pronounced Broo-
ho) which means Love, the Magician. Paco was in it!
There is a wonderful wonderful scene between Cand-
ela (Maria Rojas) and the ghost of her dead lover
(which is the part Paco was dancing). It is very exciting and passionate. Very s-e-x-y, Jessamy says. I
cannot disagree with her! There is one bit where
I think Gran might almost have turned if off had it
been on the television!*

Jessamy liked El Amor Brujo *but not as much as
I did. She prefers the flamenco numbers because she*

72

says some of the rest is like watered-down ballet. I expect she is right and that I am just prejudiced because of who was in it.

He didn't dance any solos tonight. Instead, Carlos Miguel did one. He too is an excellent dancer. He looks very much like Paco, only older. Very proud and haughty and a little bit stern. I wonder if they can be related?

Afterwards we waited outside the stage door again. We saw Maria Rojas, Luis Martín, Pepe Ruiz, Rosita Romero and lots of members of the corps, but not Paco. As we left Jessamy said, 'Perhaps on Wednesday.' What does she mean, perhaps on Wednesday???

We are certainly going to go on Wednesday, but we had already discussed this. We are going to go twice, both afternoon and evening! Jessamy has already bought the tickets. And for the Wednesday after, as well, and every Saturday that the Company are there! I am so relieved that Jessamy likes it as much as I do ecause although I would still go by myself I wouldn't be brave enough to wait at the stage door if she wasn't there with me.

But why did she say 'Maybe on Wednesday'? I do hope she hasn't guessed!

Monday 11 April
I have got a Spanish phrase book from the library. I wanted to find a real teach-yourself book but there wasn't one. It is very frustrating, just as I have grown interested. But I have learnt a few phrases already. Buenos dias *is good day, and* buenas noches *is good*

night, and muchas gracias *is thank you. Now I will say* buenas noches! *and go to bed.*

Tuesday 12 April
I have discovered who took the Teach Yourself Spanish *book out of the library. It was Jessamy! I went round to see her after work and found her surrounded by all these books on Spain and Spanish dancing. She is also trying to teach herself Spanish! She has given me the teach-yourself book as she has a record, which she says is better. We listened to some of it and I have learnt a few more phrases.* Cuanto es? (*How much is it?*). Es verdad? (*Is that so?*) Como esta usted? (*How are you?*) Etc.

Jessamy says it is dead easy and that by the time we go back next term she is going to be fluent. I expect she probably will be as she has more time to learn than I do and is braver about speaking it. She has suggested that I go round every Sunday and we do nothing but talk Spanish together.

I know why I want to learn it, but why does Jessamy?

Thursday 14 April
Yesterday (ayer) *we went to the theatre* (teatro) *again* (de nuevo). *We went twice! Paco danced his* zapateado *in the evening as well as in the afternoon. I think I almost know it off by heart. He also did a lovely gentle Inca dance called* Huayno *and a fiery one called* Zorongo *with Maria Rojas. He dances a lot with Maria Rojas. I wonder if she is his girlfriend?*

74

No! I don't want her to be. Jessamy still thinks she is beautiful but she is definitely fat.

There is a song in Zorongo *by someone called Federico Garcia Lorca, who the programme says was a famous Spanish poet who was murdered. It is very passionate and haunting. These are the words:*

'La luna es un pozo chico,
Las flores no valen nada.
Lo que valen son tus brazos
Cuando de noche me abrazan.'

I think it is a love song and I am learning it by heart because it is so beautiful.

We waited at the stage door as usual and this time Paco came out! He was wearing a short denim jacket, white shirt, blue jeans and high-heeled boots. He is one of those people who look just as exotic off stage as on. All the crowd mobbed him, wanting his autograph, and I felt very smug on account of Jessamy already having got it for me. As we stood watching he suddenly saw us and smiled!!! I nearly died, but I suppose it was Jessamy he was doing it to rather than me. He obviously remembers her. Jessamy is memorable. She is not only pretty but has a very strong personality which I think is reflected in her features. I am just small and nondescript and totally insignificant. All I can do is dance. I don't expect Paco even noticed that I was there.

Jessamy said as we walked back to the tube, 'Well! That should have made you happy.' Does this mean she has guessed???? Oh, I do hope not! She will only tease me.

Friday 15 April

Ken rang up this evening. He is so nice! I do like him. He said he's going to the second performance tomorrow and did Jessamy and I want to join him afterwards for supper? Of course I said yes! I rang Jessamy to tell her and she said, 'Oh, I'd forgotten that we're meant to be keeping an eye on him.'

Gran is fussed as usual about me being out late but I am going to go back with Jessamy and stay the night. In the morning we are going to practise our Spanish!

Sunday 17 April

Jessamy has guessed. I knew she would. She said she guessed almost right from the very beginning. Now she won't stop teasing me. She keeps saying things like 'How can you be so unfaithful?' meaning to Saul, and threatening to tell him. I don't think that she will – though she might – but anyway I am not being unfaithful. I still think Saul is one of the really great dancers of this century and it is still my ambition to dance with him one day and I still think he is heavenly and gorgeous and divine and every bit as nice as Ken, though in a different sort of way – Ken is quieter and easier to talk to. Saul is more like Jessamy, always up-front and making jokes and everyone taking notice of him – BUT it is not the same as I feel about Paco. I have always, for ages and ages, dreamt of dancing with Saul. I don't dream of dancing with Paco as I think it is very unlikely that I ever could (unfortunately).

Actually that is not true. Just because it is unlikely

it does not stop me dreaming about it. I dream about dancing with him and I dream about – doing other things with him! I cannot really describe adequately what I feel. Jessamy says that it is just a crush, because he is handsome and v-e-r-y s-e-x-y. But it is more than that! He is also a wonderful, brilliant dancer. Jessamy doesn't understand what it is to have these sorts of feelings. In the past I have tried to pull her leg about boys, but she has never really felt about any of them the way I feel about Paco.

He danced his zapateado *again last night. It is a great favourite with the audience, and with the critics too. Eric Lauder wrote in the paper that 'Paco Gonzalez, with his superb control and dazzling technique, conjures up memories of the great Antonio, a legend in the world of Spanish dance.' I must find out more about Antonio!*

Ken took us for a meal afterwards in a restaurant near the theatre and I ate far too much! I think Jessamy has forgotten about her diet because she ate even more than I did. Just lately she has stopped being obsessed about how much she weighs, which I expect can only be a good thing.

Ken told us about being allowed in to watch rehearsals and make sketches. He said that Paco is Carlos Miguel's son and that he and his father often have blazing rows and swear at each other in front of the whole Company! Ken can't speak very much Spanish and so he doesn't know what the rows are about. He seems to think it is probably just a matter of temperament. He says that Carlos Miguel is 'autocratic' and expects always to have his own way (like

Madam) and that Paco is rebellious. He says they are also both very mercurial, by which I think he means quick-tempered.

It is fascinating hearing all these details. Oh, but Jessamy made me feel so ashamed! There are times when she can be so pushy. She actually asked Ken if we could go along to a rehearsal with him. I could see that he was embarrassed and didn't know what to say. In the end he muttered that he didn't think it would be wise of him to push his luck. He said the only reason they had let him go was that he was a friend of Saul's. He said. 'They're like one big quarrel-some family, but very tight-knit. They don't really like outsiders getting in on the act.' Even then Jessamy couldn't just let it drop. She said, 'You could always try. If you said I was Saul's sister?' It embarrassed me as well as Ken. She really oughtn't to put people on the spot like that. Specially Ken, when he's been so kind.

I told her this in the cab on the way home but she just tossed her head in that way she has – sometimes I think Jessamy doesn't care about anything – and said, 'I don't see why he can't just ask. Saul would.' I pointed out that Saul was a famous dancer whereas Ken was still a struggling artist, to which Jessamy retorted that 'if you never ask, you'll never get.'

I think Jessamy will always get. She is that sort of person.

Monday 18 April

I forgot to mention that Ken says most of Carlos Miguel's company are 'gitanos' . . . real gypsies! That explains why they have so much fire and passion.

Wednesday 20 April

Went to two performances and waited outside the stage door as usual but Paco didn't appear. Luis did. He recognises us and has become quiet friendly. He said, 'Here again?' and Jessamy grinned and said, 'Yes, we're fans.' I was on tenter-hooks in case she went and said something blush-making about me waiting to see Paco, but thank goodness she didn't!

We had a bit of an argument on the way home because Jessamy was saying again about Maria Rojas being so beautiful. I said I thought she was fat and Jessamy grew quite cross and said that she wasn't in the least bit fat, she was a perfectly normal female shape. I said, 'She's got a big bottom,' and Jessamy snapped, 'Yes and she's got boobs as well! Women do have, you know.'

I said, 'Not that size. Not in ballet,' and Jessamy said this wasn't ballet and I said no, but it was still dancing, whereupon Jessamy shouted that she was sick and tired of everyone expecting dancers to look like hosepipes, which fortunately made us both giggle and saved it from developing into a full-scale row.

I wonder if Jessamy is still secretly worried about her weight? She is terribly sensitive about it.

Friday 22 April

Today when we were filling shelves one of the girls from Upfield asked me if I was a dancer. When I said yes she said, 'I thought you had to be. You look like a dancer... all thin and stick-like.' Oh, I can't wait to stop doing this horrible job and get back to ballet school! But I have decided I must still work on Thursday evenings and Saturdays. I can't expect Gran to go on paying for everything; not if I want to keep visiting the theatre, which I do. The Company is only here for another two weeks before going on tour. I want to go as often as I can!

Saturday 23 April

A truly wonderful evening! El Amor Brujo, which I adore, and the zapateado. And I saw Paco afterwards! He didn't see us, or if he did he didn't take any notice. But I think he was in too much of a rage. Something must have upset him – perhaps one of those blazing rows with his father – because he came storming out, carrying his jacket over his shoulder, angrily shouting something in Spanish to someone inside, though I couldn't see who. Instead of stopping like he usually does to give autographs he simply strode straight past, and when people started crowding him he yelled at them to 'Stop raping me!' which Jessamy thought was funny and started giggling, and I suppose it was in a way, but I wish I knew what had happened. Maybe Ken will tell me.

Sunday 24 April

Jessamy says, if you want to find out, why not ring and ask? She says, 'You can't be shy of ringing Ken.'

Half an hour later. I rang him! But he doesn't know. He says his Spanish isn't good enough to follow all the ins and outs, but from what he can gather he thinks that Paco may be threatening to leave the Company.

I wish now that I hadn't rung. I don't think I could bear it if Paco were not there.

Monday 25 April

It is such a relief to be back at ballet school. Every minute I'm not there just seems the most terrible waste of time (except when I'm at the theatre).

Miss Fane, weighing and measuring us, said 'Well, Jessamy! At least you haven't gained anything.' Actually she had managed to lose two and a half kilos so Miss Fane wasn't really being fair, but I suppose she doesn't think that two and a half kilos is enough. Jessamy certainly isn't fat, or even plump, though it has to be admitted she isn't as thin as she used to be.

I asked her (very tactfully) whether she had given up on her diet and she said yes, she couldn't be bothered with it. So then I said, 'What about the jogging?' and it seems she couldn't be bothered with that either. She said, 'It's too boring, on one's own.' Now I feel guilty because of not going with her. I could have done, if I'd made an effort. I tried apologising but Jessamy said there wasn't any need. She said, 'I have decided that if you're not cut out to be sylph-like then it's pointless to keep on fighting a losing battle.'

This is the first time I have ever known Jessamy

not to do something she set out to do. It is most unlike her.

Tuesday 26 April
Today Miss Fane told us about the Bath Festival of Dance. It seems the school has been invited to put on a production! Madam is going to choose who is to appear in it. Ginny said to me, 'You'll be in it 'cause of being one of Madam's faves.' I know I'm in her special class, but so are lots of others now so I don't think it does to take things for granted. I am certainly not going to!

Wednesday 27 April
Went to the evening performance and I was dead scared in case Paco wasn't there, but he was, and danced something brilliant called Fandango, *all stamping and snapping and crashing down on to his knees, which pleased Jessamy because it was flamenco. However, we didn't see him afterwards, which is always an anti-climax, so although it was a good evening it wasn't absolutely one of the best. But there is still Saturday!*

Thursday 28 April
Today in Character Mr Badowski announced that we were going to learn some of the dances from Tricorne. *He advised us to go and take a look at the Spanish dancing at the Fountain!!! Jessamy told him about us going there every week and he said in that case he would expect 'some of the real thing' from us.*

Jessamy is so good at Character. I have seen just as

much Spanish dancing as she has but she seems to have a feel for it and I don't. I could tell that Mr Badowski was really impressed. I felt horridly and nastily envious as I imagined Jessamy dancing a flamenco with Paco.

I wish I had black hair!

Friday 29 April
Jessamy is up to something. I know she is. Today Mr Badowski announced there were some free tickets for the Spanish dance for tomorrow afternoon and any student wanting one should go to the office straight away. Jessamy wasn't there because of seeing the physio so I went rushing down to grab a couple before they all went. When Jessamy appeared I showed them to her, thinking she'd be as overjoyed as I was, but instead she said, 'Oh! I can't go tomorrow afternoon.' When I said why not she actually turned a bit pink and said 'Because I can't. I've got something else to do.' But she won't tell me what!

It's worrying because last time she went all secretive on me was when she was going ice skating with Ginny's cousin. But she only did that because of Madam keeping on overlooking her and not giving her proper parts. Surely now she's one of Madam's specials she wouldn't go and do anything silly?

Anyway, I'm still going to go tomorrow afternoon. Maggot is going to come with me. I don't care about the horrible supermarket! I shall say that I'm ill. Gran would have a fit if she knew, she would say it was dishonourable, but I can't help it. This is far more important.

Saturday 30 April
*THE MOST WONDERFUL DAY OF MY LIFE
SO FAR!*

Oh, and I thought at first it was going to be nothing but one huge enormous disappointment because the opening ballet was Carmen and Paco wasn't in it! He was supposed to be, his name was in the programme, but Luis took his place. There wasn't any announcement or anything, so I absolutely wasn't prepared for it. It was the most terrible shock, I really thought he'd gone and walked out. I had to explain to Maggot that although Luis is quite good he is not a patch on Paco. I kept praying all through that when it came to his zapateado he would be there as usual, but he wasn't! It was Carlos Miguel and I didn't enjoy it one little bit because of worrying.

Afterwards Maggot was going on about how wonderful it was, and especially the last number (the zapateado) and I couldn't get up any enthusiasm at all. Fortunately she didn't want to go and hang about the stage door, which was just as well as I don't think I could have faced it. I felt as if I had stones in the pit of my stomach. Instead she wanted to go somewhere and have a Coke, so I said all right, but all the time my heart was nearly bursting because of this fixed belief I had that I was never going to see him again.

Then all of a sudden, as we were walking down a side street, he appeared! He was walking quite fast towards the theatre, just wearing ordinary jeans and a sweater, but of course I recognised him immediately. And as he went past he smiled at me! He actually

84

smiled at me! Me, without Jessamy! I know I'm not imagining it because Maggot said 'Who was that?' in a gaping sort of tone as if she couldn't believe that I would know anyone so totally gorgeous. I said as carelessly as I could (but I know that I blushed) 'That was Paco Gonzalez, one of the leading dancers,' and Maggot said, 'He smiled at you!'

He did, he did! And later, when I met Jessamy and went back for the second performance (which we'd already bought tickets for) he was there on stage and dancing better than ever, the sparks were absolutely flying, and I was in heaven.

We didn't see him again afterwards, but I didn't mind that. I know that he's still there – and I know that he recognises me!

I am seriously considering dyeing my hair.

6

Jessamy, happily heel-and-toe tapping round her bedroom, rattling her castanets more or less in some sort of time, came to a halt as the front door bell rang. That must be Karen! They were going to spend the whole of Sunday morning practising their Spanish.

Hastily she raced downstairs before Dad could get there. Karen was shy of Dad, and Dad knew it. He could never resist making these really idiotic comments, and then, of course, she got even more shy and started blushing, which just made Dad a hundred times worse. In many ways, thought Jessamy, Dad was a bit of a bully. You had to stand up to him, like Mum and Jessamy.

She threw open the front door.

'Good! You're early! I th –' Jessamy stopped. 'What's the matter?' she said. 'What's happened?'

Karen stood there on the doorstep, a pathetic waif with drooping shoulders and downcast eyes. She had a scarf tied peasantwise over her head, hiding her hair.

'It's not your gran?' whispered Jessamy.

Karen's gran was quite old and rather fragile. She suffered from arthritis and something called angina, which was to do with the heart.

'She hasn't – '

Jessamy couldn't bring herself to say it. But Karen shook her head; emphatically yet none the less tragically. Jessamy's brain whirled, seeking explanations.

'I know! Ken rang . . . Paco's left the company!'

'*No*!' The cry came wailing out, querulous with protest. How could Jessamy even suggest such a thing?

'So what is it? Something to do with ballet?'

Another thought occurred. Madam had rung – had written a letter – had said that Karen's scholarship was not going to be renewed and that –

No! That was too terrible even to be contemplated. *Of course* Karen's scholarship would be renewed.

'Tell me!' said Jessamy. 'Don't keep me in suspense!'

'Oh, Jessamy!' Karen pulled off her headscarf and burst into tears. 'Look what I've done!'

Jessamy stared; she couldn't help it. Karen's bright flaxen hair was now a dull and muddy brown.

'How did you do it?' gasped Jessamy.

'I bought this s-stuff in a b-bottle!'

'But what – oh, look, let's get in!'

Jessamy hustled Karen through the door and upstairs to her bedroom before either Mum or Dad could appear and start making stupid remarks.

'Does your gran know?'

'N-no, she's still in b-bed!'

'So when did you do it?'

'This m-morning. When I g-got up.' Karen scrubbed at her eyes. 'There was this stuff that said r-raven b-black and I p-put it on and l-left it and – oh, Jessamy!' She dissolved all over again. 'What am I going to do?'

Jessamy sat down cross-legged on the bed and solemnly considered Karen's muddy brown locks.

'Was it an actual dye? Or just a rinse?'

'Just a r-rinse, I th-think.'

'So maybe it might wash out.'

'I tried! It doesn't!'

'It might if we keep *on* trying. Let's go into the bathroom!'

They spent most of the morning in the bathroom. Karen worried that someone might come bursting in, but Mum and Dad had a bathroom of their own, opening off their bedroom, and 'There isn't anyone else in the house,' Jessamy assured her. 'Just hold still and don't *panic*.'

After six full hair washings and a great many rinsings, using up one entire bottle of shampoo and half a bottle of conditioner, Karen was almost, but not quite, back to normal. If you didn't know that her hair was usually flaxen, it wouldn't occur to you that there was anything amiss.

'It's just a bit . . . yellowish,' said Jessamy, proud of her handiwork.

Karen took one look at herself in the mirror and collapsed yet again in tears.

'It looks like sick!'

Jessamy was affronted: this was a slur on her hairdressing skills.

'It's better than it was before.'

'It's horrible!'

'It'll grow out. What I don't understand,' said Jessamy, 'is what on earth you did it for?'

Two little spots of pink appeared on Karen's cheeks.

'I thought it might be better if I had black hair.'

'Why?'

'Well, because – because it shows up better on stage!'

It did show up better on stage; but that wasn't the reason.

'You'll never get to dance with him, you know.' Jessamy said it kindly. 'Nothing's ever going to turn you into a Spanish dancer.'

'Oh! No. Well, of course, I know *that*,' said Karen, blushing right up to the roots of her buttercup locks.

'I have come to the conclusion,' said Jessamy, 'that it simply isn't any use trying to turn yourself into something you're not. You just have to accept your limitations,' said Jessamy, sounding remarkably cheerful and untroubled by it. 'You might not realise it, but I used to envy you terribly up until just a very short time ago.'

'You envied *me*?' said Karen.

'Mm.' Jessamy nodded, vigorously. 'Never having to worry about fat hips or huge thighs or getting too big or – '

'I'm just puny,' said Karen.

'They like people that are puny; in ballet they do. Women, anyway,' said Jessamy, remembering what her mum had had to say on the subject. 'And then I used to envy you for being classical, 'cause I just knew I wasn't ever going to get to dance Giselle or

Sleeping Beauty, I was always going to be stuck as the mouldy old Lilac Fairy or a Bluebird or something. And then I envied you 'cause everyone did for being one of Madam's faves – '

'But you got into her special class ages ago!' protested Karen.

'I know, but I'm not one of her *faves*. And I won't ever be. But it doesn't bother me now,' said Jessamy, most curiously serene. 'I don't mind any more. I know I'm not cut out for classical ballet.'

'*Jessamy*!' Karen's voice was almost piercing in its agony. 'You can't say that!'

'I can,' said Jessamy. 'I just have. Watch my lips . . . *I am not cut out for classical ballet.*'

'But – ' Karen floundered. 'You're one of the best dancers in the school!'

'Oh, I think I'm a good dancer,' said Jessamy. She had never suffered from false modesty. 'I just don't necessarily think that I'm a good *ballet* dancer. I'm the wrong shape – or at least, I'm going to be – and I've got the wrong temperament. Which is why I don't always see eye to eye with Madam, 'cause she likes everything done her way and if you don't do it her way you'll never be asked to join the Company, and this is what I have come to realise,' said Jessamy. 'It's all right for the boys; they can be rebellious. Saul used to be, and Madam thinks he's the cat's whiskers. But if you're a girl, you've got to conform. And I just can't,' said Jessamy. 'It's as simple as that.'

Karen was staring at her, eyes wide with consternation. 'So what are you going to do?'

'Oh, I shall find something.'

'You'll still dance?'

'I shall always do that,' said Jessamy.

'Modern?'

'Dunno. Haven't decided yet.' Jessamy grinned. 'Can't say that it bothers me.'

'It bothers me!' wailed Karen.

'Well, don't let it! I think it's exciting – like sailing off to discover America. I've been doing ballet for almost twelve years,' said Jessamy. 'And just lately it's depressed me, thinking I might still be doing it in another twelve.'

'It would depress me if I thought I might not be,' said Karen.

'Yes, well, that's the difference between us.' Jessamy bounced herself off the bed and raced across to put on her record of *Teach Yourself Spanish*. *'Debemos hablar español!'*

Monday 2 May

I wish I knew what Jessamy was up to. There is definitely something going on but she is still being secretive. She told me yesterday that she doesn't think she's cut out to be a ballet dancer, which is complete rubbish I think. Today I asked her if she'd said anything to her parents and she said, 'I can't. Not yet. I'm waiting.' But when I said, 'Waiting for what?' she wouldn't tell me.

My hair still looks like sick. Ginny said, 'Oh, look, that is brilliant! Karen has dyed her hair the colour of dog's vomit,' and of course everyone wanted to know what I'd done it for. I said that I had found this stuff in a bottle and thought that it was just ordinary

91

shampoo, whereupon Ginny groaned and Lorraine rolled her eyes as if to say, 'Trust her!'

They obviously think I am stupid and they are quite right. I am. Stupid stupid STUPID! How could I ever hope to dance with Paco?

'I need a job,' announced Jessamy, as she and Karen travelled in together on Tuesday morning.

'*You* do?' Karen was astonished. Jessamy was never kept short of money! She even had her own building society account.

'I've got to start working. Do you think they'd have anything at your place?'

'I could ask,' said Karen, 'but I don't think so. Unless they'd take you instead of me.'

'Instead of you?' It was Jessamy's turn to be surprised. 'Why? Are you stopping?'

'I'm still doing Thursday, but not Saturdays. Gran says it's too much.'

'It wouldn't be too much for me,' said Jessamy. Karen had to help her gran with the housework and shopping, on account of her gran's arthritis. Jessamy was spoiled: she hardly had to lift a finger. 'But anyway, Saturday's no good. I can't work on a Saturday.'

'Why's that?' said Karen, striving to sound casual.

'Got other things to do.'

'Like what?'

'My, aren't we nosy!' said Jessamy.

Karen pursed her lips as a sign of disapproval.

'Look, I *will* tell you,' said Jessamy, 'but not just at the moment.'

'What's so secret about it? Are you going out with a boy?'

Jessamy laughed and tossed her head, but not before Karen had had time to glimpse a touch of redness in her cheeks. It was unlike Jessamy to blush.

'I suppose you are,' grumbled Karen. 'Well, you needn't think I'm interested.'

'No! You'd rather worship from afar. All these mad passions ... first it was Nureyev, then it was Saul, now it's Paco ... but you never actually *do* anything about it!'

'Well, what could I do?' cried Karen.

'Draw attention to yourself – make them notice you. I would,' said Jessamy.

'Yes, and then you'd look stupid!'

'Not as stupid as you do, going all red and goopy. Honestly,' said Jessamy. 'Why don't you go and talk to him?'

''Cause I think it would be presumptuous.'

'Stupid! Of course it wouldn't. Why have you got such a low opinion of yourself? He's not that much older than you are, and you'll be just as great a dancer as he is, one day.'

Karen heaved a sigh. It was really very difficult, maintaining any sort of anger against Jessamy. One minute she was grossly insulting you – all red and goopy! – and the next she was paying you extravagant compliments.

'If ever I *am* a great dancer, which I don't expect I will be –'

'Yes, you will!'

93

'Well, then, I'd go and talk to anybody,' said Karen. 'But while I'm still just *me* – '

'Oh, fiddle faddle!' said Jessamy. (It was an expression she had picked up from her mother.) 'He'd probably be only too happy to have a nice little blonde English señorita go up and say hallo to him.'

But I'm not blonde, thought Karen; I'm *yellow*!

Later that day Miss Fane announced that Madam would be holding a special audition class for senior pupils at four o'clock that Saturday afternoon in Studio A.

'It's an open audition, for anyone who is interested in appearing at the Festival. But of course,' said Miss Fane, 'I shall expect you all to attend.'

'Saturday afternoon,' murmured Karen. She glanced slyly at Jessamy. 'You'll have to tell your boyfriend you can't see him.'

'I haven't got a boyfriend!' snapped Jessamy.

Friday 6 May

Jessamy swears she hasn't got a boyfriend, but I don't believe her. She is definitely hiding something. She also says that she has found a job, washing up in the Tea Room at Markham's after school on Thursdays. I can't imagine Jessamy washing up! I shouldn't even think she knows how to. But what does she need a job for?

I don't know whether I shall dare go and wait at the stage door tomorrow with my hair being all yellow.

Sunday 8 May

Yesterday was Madam's special audition class for the Festival. Miss Fane said just to treat it as an ordinary class, but of course nobody could. We all think that the people she chooses are the ones that are going to be kept on, and the ones she doesn't choose are the ones that are going to be thrown out . . .

Jessamy was late!!! I thought at first she wasn't going to turn up at all because she still hadn't arrived by the time most of us were ready, but then as we were walking along the corridor Maggot suddenly looked out of the window and saw her racing up the road and I thought that if she got changed really quickly she could probably make it, though it's not a good idea, I don't think, to be rushed before something important like an audition class. On the other hand, Jessamy doesn't suffer from nerves like I do so maybe she doesn't mind being rushed.

Anyway I kept expecting her to come bursting in, and when she didn't I just couldn't think what had happened to her and I was getting really worried because Madam was due to arrive at any moment. In the end she turned up – Jessamy I mean – with about one split second to spare, all red and panting and in a simply terrible state. Now of course, in spite of telling me that she isn't cut out to be a ballet dancer she's dead scared in case she did a bad class and doesn't get chosen. Why does Jessamy always want everything both ways???

But there's something which puzzles me. Jessamy said the reason she only reached the studio with a second to spare was that she didn't realise the studio had been changed from Studio A to Studio E, and so she'd gone charging off in the wrong direction and had to come charging all the way back again to try and find out what was happening. In the end she'd discovered Miss Fane's notice pinned on the notice-board. But I'd specially left a note stuck to her locker! I'd done it for that very reason. I knew she wouldn't have realised and wouldn't have time to find out. Jessamy swears however that there wasn't any note. She says she would have seen it, and that is what I would have thought. It is a mystery.

I didn't go and wait at the stage door. I couldn't bear the thought of Paco seeing me with my hair like this. Jessamy says I am completely idiotic and that he wouldn't even notice. I expect what she probably means is that he wouldn't notice me anyway, whatever colour my hair was. At first she said that she was going to wait whether I did or not, but then at the last minute she changed her mind and we just trailed dismally home. I was feeling dismal because of my hair and because of not seeing Paco, and Jessamy was feeling dismal, I suppose, because of being late for Madam. I know that she is worried; I can always tell, even though outwardly she pretends not to care.

I don't think that I am worried. I think I did a good class. But it doesn't do to count one's chickens. I shall wait and see.

Monday 9 May
I believe I may have solved the mystery of what happened to the note that I stuck on Jessamy's locker. I was awake half last night thinking about it, because

although Jessamy says it was her fault for being late in the first place, I still felt bad about it. And then I remembered . . . when Maggot saw Jessamy rushing up the road she said, 'Oh, look! There she is!' and I said thank goodness, she'd just about make it, and it was at that moment that Ginny suddenly screeched she'd left her mascot behind and went racing off to fetch it. But Nella says she's almost certain Ginny had it with her all the time. It's a little pink cuddly toy and Nella swears she had it wrapped up in her towel.

When I told Jessamy she just pulled a face and said that she and Ginny had always been rivals – as if you expect someone who's a rival to play mean tricks. Jessamy says I am still naïve and that I will learn. But I don't like to think of ballet being full of people like that!

Wednesday 11 May
Went to see Paco for almost the last time . . . the evening was completely ruined by my dwelling on the fact that after Saturday the Company won't be here. They are going off on tour, all over the British Isles. It is a comfort, though only a small one, that at least they will still be in the same country. But oh, how am I going to live without seeing him???

Thursday 12 May
Still haven't heard who is going to dance at the Festival. Everyone is saying glumly, 'I don't expect I'll be chosen.' Ginny said again, 'Of course she will,' nodding in my direction. 'She's one of Madam's faves.' I

wish she would stop saying this! It makes me feel awful and anyway it is tempting providence.

Friday 13 May
Still haven't heard. But special rehearsals start next week!!!

Sunday 15 May
I am utterly miserable: I have seen Paco for the last time. Well, not quite the last time and that is my one ray of hope and the only thing that keeps me going. We have discovered that in August they are appearing in Croydon, at the Fairfield Hall! Jessamy says that Croydon is only a short train journey away, and so we are going to book tickets immediately. Jessamy wants to go just as much as I do and seems almost as bereft, if that is the word. So much so that for a moment I almost wondered whether there was some-one in the Company that she feels about as I feel about Paco, and in fact I have been racking my brains to think who it could be.

I don't think she would fall for Luis, because although he is nice he is really quite ordinary and not in the same class as Paco or Carlos Miguel when it comes to dancing. Pepe Ruiz (I have discovered from Ken that he is Paco's cousin) is utterly gorgeous, and Rafael Romero is also quite good-looking, and they are excellent dancers, but on the other hand Jessamy hasn't made any attempt to get their autographs or make them take notice of her, which is what she said she would do, so maybe it's just that she is going to miss the dancing. I will miss it too, but not nearly as much as I shall miss Paco. I keep having these dreams that we are dancing together, and sometimes it is Spanish dancing and sometimes it is ballet, but either way I know it is impossible. But I still can't stop thinking about him.

Oh, why do I always have to go and spoil things by letting misery intrude? Tonight should have been such fun! All the Company were in party mood and kept doing ridiculous things to make each other laugh. In the Basque ballet Pepe Ruiz stole the glass that the girls jump on and started jumping on and off it himself! And Paco went and pretended to flirt with Carlos Miguel, which was really funny because Carlos Miguel looked absolutely outraged and of course lots of people in the audience didn't know that he is Paco's father! And afterwards there was this huge crowd at the stage door and they were all waving and shouting, and members of the Company came out and waved back, and Luis saw us and winked and Paco smiled at us – at us, me and Jessamy – and Jessamy called out Buena suerte! *which she says means good luck. (She thinks it means good luck. How awful if it doesn't! But Jessamy doesn't care.)*

Now it is all over and all I have is his photograph. If it weren't for seeing him again in Croydon, I don't think I could bear it.

Monday 16 May
The lists went up and Jessamy and I are both dancing leads! Jessamy is in Tarantella *and I am in* Spring Sonata, *which is one of Madam's own ballets which the Company premiered last year. Maggot and Nella*

both have small solos and so does Lorraine. Ginny on the other hand has quite a large one, which still doesn't stop her being furious (she thinks she ought to have a lead) especially after the failure of her ploy to get Jessamy expelled, or at any rate left out of the Festival. The more I think about it, the more convinced I am that it was what she went back to the changing room for.

I am so glad we have both been chosen! I wouldn't have been nearly so happy if it had only been me. I think Jessamy is pleased too, though she does come out with some very odd things. She said to me on the way home, very seriously, 'You see, I have to prove myself. Unless I can prove myself –' And then she stopped and I said 'What?' But she just shook her head and said, 'It would make things even more difficult.'

She has been in such a strange mood just lately, all excited and secretive and somehow full of purpose. But happy. I wish I knew what was going on!

Tuesday 17 May
There are another seventy-nine days before I can see Paco . . .

7

'Thursdays?' Jessamy's voice rose high with dismay. 'Special rehearsals on Thursdays?'

'After school,' said Nella. 'What's wrong with that?'

'I work on Thursdays!'

'Work?' Ginny looked at her, amused. 'Why? Don't your parents give you any pocket money?'

Jessamy ignored her. 'Of all the days to go and choose!' Seven days in the week, and they had to go and pick on Thursdays. Just as Jessamy had it all nicely arranged! 'What about you?' She turned to Karen. 'You work on Thursdays, as well!'

'I'll see if I can change to Saturdays,' said Karen. 'Maybe you could.'

'Saturdays aren't any good!' wailed Jessamy. 'I can't work on Saturdays!'

Now what was she going to do? Her building society account wouldn't last for ever. Oh! Why did life have to be so complicated?

'It's all right,' she announced, beaming, to Karen, as they met up at the tube the next day. 'I went in to see them and they said I could start later.'

Karen, whose head had been filled with the strains of *Spring Sonata*, stared at her in bewilderment.

'Who did?'

'Markham's. They said I could go in at seven and work till nine.'

'Is that a good idea?' Karen sounded doubtful. 'After being at school all day and doing an extra rehearsal?'

'I don't know, but I've got to. I need the money.' She had already taken loads out of her building society book as it was. If ever Mum got to see it there would be trouble. The money was supposed to be savings, for when she was older. Mum didn't mind her just taking out the odd little bit now and again for something special, but she wasn't supposed to run it down to nothing.

Karen shook her head.

'You'll get worn out,' she said.

'No, I won't! I've got loads of energy. What wears me out is when I'm *not* using it, not when I am. I get really bored,' said Jessamy, 'if I'm not doing things.'

'Don't you get bored washing up?'

'No, 'cause it's only two hours and there's lots of other people to talk to. It's quite fun, really.'

'Stocking shelves isn't fun,' said Karen. 'I'm glad I've had to stop.'

'Stopped *completely*?'

'Until the holidays, then I expect I'll have to go back. Gran said if I was having extra rehearsals I wasn't to do anything else.'

'Wrapped in cotton wool!' jeered Jessamy; but she knew that wasn't fair. If she had to do all the housework and the shopping that Karen did, she probably wouldn't find it such fun having to go into

102

Markham's and spend two hours washing up. 'Is your gran coming to the performance?'

'She's coming to see us in London. Are your mum and dad?'

'Yes. They were talking of coming to Bath, as well, then they decided not to, thank goodness!'

'Why thank goodness?' said Karen.

'Well – ' Jessamy pulled a face. 'It'll be more like proper touring if we're by ourselves.'

They were giving the first performance at the Company's own theatre, the Fountain, before travelling down to Bath for their appearance at the Festival.

'I wish we could be there for a whole week!' said Jessamy.

'Angie says we're lucky we're there at all.'

'Yes.' Jessamy nodded, soberly. Angie was one of the ones who hadn't been chosen. However could I have faced Mum and Dad, she thought, if that had happened to me? Mum and Dad were expecting so much of her! It wasn't enough that they had a son who was a leading dancer: they wanted Jessamy to be one, as well.

It had been a great disappointment to them when Jacquetta had opted out; now Jessamy was paying the price. Mum had said to her only the other day, when Jessamy had broken the good news about the Festival, 'I'm so relieved that at last you're starting to fulfil your potential! We've never had any doubts as to your ability, but I confess there have been times when we've wondered whether you had the staying power.' And then she had given Jessamy one of her rare affectionate hugs and said, 'I have a feeling this is going to be a turning point . . . we'll end up being just as proud of you as we are of Saul!'

It had made little nervous flitters go twitching down Jessamy's spine. If Mum only knew what she was doing with all that money from the building society . . .

Saul rang unexpectedly one night from Paris.

'Hi!' he said. 'Congratulations! I hear you've got yourself in Madam's good books at last.'

'Who told you that?' said Jessamy. 'Have you been talking to Mum?'

'Nope.'

'So who told you?'

'Ha! Wouldn't you like to know?'

'Well, I would,' said Jessamy, ''cause as a matter of fact I don't think Madam approves of me any more than she ever did.'

'It's just that you're too good a dancer to ignore.'

Thinking about it, Jessamy supposed that perhaps that was true. She *was* a good dancer, she knew that she was! But she also knew that her temperament and Madam's were fated to clash. Paco Gonzalez could shout at Carlos Miguel and even swear at him, and they could still go on working together. That wasn't possible with Madam. Not that Jessamy had ever wanted to swear, but there were times, quite definitely, when she would have liked to shout 'I'm *me*! Not a clockwork toy!' But Madam held the key, and only a few favourites, such as Saul, were allowed a life of their own.

'So who *did* tell you?' said Jessamy.

'Ken. He just rang me.'

And how did Ken know? Karen must have spoken to him. What a sly creature Karen was at times! Doing things on her own without telling Jessamy. (Of course, Jessamy did things on her own, too, but that was different. Jessamy had a reason.)

'Are you keeping an eye on him for me as you promised?'

'I don't think he needs an eye kept on him,' said Jessamy. 'I think Ken is trustworthy.'

Saul chuckled. 'You'd better be right, or I shall hold you personally responsible!'

'If you ask me,' said Jessamy, 'you're the one that needs an eye kept on him.' And then, before Saul had a chance to tell her not to be cheeky: 'When are you coming back?'

'The day before the Festival. I thought we might pop down and have a look at you.'

'Heavens!' said Jessamy. 'Karen will freak if she knows you're in the audience!'

'You, of course, will remain completely unmoved.'

'No, I won't, but I'm not soppy over you like she is.'

'More's the pity.'

'Actually – ' Jessamy giggled – 'she's got this mad crush just at the moment on one of the Spanish dancers.'

'So what? Don't knock it! At your age people ought to have mad crushes.'

'I,' said Jessamy, loftily, 'have *never* had one.'

'So that's your loss!'

'Huh!' said Jessamy.

She didn't want to go all drippy and gooey-eyed, thank you very much! Jessamy had goals to pursue; she couldn't afford to fritter away her energies in pointless daydreaming. (She *knew* that Karen daydreamed. Not in dance classes, of course; but in maths and French and geography and sitting on the tube and lying in the bath and before going to sleep and first thing on waking up. Practically her entire life, when she wasn't dancing, was taken up with thoughts of Paco. And it was all in vain, for how could she ever hope to dance with him? Jessamy stood more chance than Karen did!)

The Bath Festival of Dance took place in the middle of July. It was a week-long event and the students of the City Ballet School were scheduled for performances on Saturday afternoon and Saturday evening, which meant travelling down the day before and travelling back the day after and staying in a hotel for the two nights in between.

'Almost like a real mini-tour,' said Maggot, happily.

Maggot wasn't dancing a lead, only an extremely small solo, but was content simply to have been chosen. Ginny, on the other hand, who was dancing a rather large solo, remained disgruntled and put out. Many pointed references were made by both her and Lorraine to 'friends in high places', meaning Jessamy's parents and Saul.

'We all know,' said Ginny, 'how useful it is to have connections.'

'Essential, I'd say,' said Lorraine.

'Have you got connections?' demanded Maggot, in a loud aggrieved voice of Karen. 'I must say it's very sneaky of you never to have told us about them!'

'Some people,' muttered Ginny, 'just suck up to the ones that have.'

'Oh!' Maggot's face cleared. 'Is that the way it's done? I wish someone had told me before. I suppose it's too late now?' She dropped to her knees and began crawling across the floor towards Jessamy. 'Dear sweet Jessamy, let me suck your toes!'

Somebody sniggered, somebody else giggled. Ginny made an impatient huffing noise.

'So *trivial*,' said Lorraine.

The Tuesday before they went off on their mini-tour they had a full dress rehearsal at the Fountain Theatre – the very first time any of them had danced there. It was sobering even for Jessamy, as she travelled across the stage in a twirl of pirouettes, to reflect that her points might be touching the very same spots as those of some of the great dancers of the past. Karen, of course, would be thinking of Saul, who was undoubtedly a great dancer of the present; but you couldn't get too excited, thought Jessamy, about treading in the footsteps of your own brother. She had always been treading in Saul's footsteps, as long as she could remember. It was time to begin marking out some of her own.

There were five ballets being performed – *Sylphides* and *L'Après Midi d'un Faune* by the students of the graduate class, *Tarantella*, *Spring Sonata* and *Tam O'Shanter* by the seniors. The dress rehearsal, contrary to all expectations, went without a hitch, which everybody said spelt trouble for the opening night. But that was just superstition, thought Jessamy, airily. Jessamy didn't believe in superstition!

On Wednesday, because it was the day of the performance, there were no normal lessons, only the usual class with Miss Fane, at eleven o'clock. After that they were free for the remainder of the day, to cope with any symptoms of stage fright in their own particular ways. People who lived near enough, such as Jessamy and Karen, went home to rest. Maggot and Nella, who lived too far away, went back with Jessamy.

'Why don't we all stick together?' Jessamy suggested to Karen; but Karen wanted to be on her own. She said that she was going to lie on her bed and try not to be sick.

'Well, it would go with your hair,' said Jessamy, though in fact Karen's hair was very nearly back to normal.

'We'll meet later at the tube?' begged Karen. 'I don't want to travel in by myself!'

They arranged to meet at five o'clock and went their separate ways, Karen to go and lie on her bed, Jessamy and the other two to sprawl in Jessamy's bedroom and talk.

'I feel,' announced Nella, 'as if I'm having a nervous breakdown.'

'Quite normal.' Jessamy, though cheerful as ever, found the need to keep herself occupied and was hammering and battering at a pair of point shoes to flatten the block and take the noise out of them.

(There was nothing worse, Mum always said, than the sound of points clop-clop-clopping across a stage.)

Nella turned a pair of soulful brown eyes upon Jessamy. 'Do you feel as if you're having a breakdown?'

'Well – no,' Jessamy admitted. 'But I know lots of people who do . . . Saul used to share a dressing room with Piet van den Berg and he said Piet just used to sit and shake.'

'I once read about someone,' volunteered Maggot, 'who used to go and nick things out of Woolworths.'

'*Nick* things?'

'Yes, you know . . . just little things, like tights or bars of chocolate or something.'

'What for?'

'"Cause it made them so nervous they forgot about having stage fright.'

'Weird,' said Jessamy, scraping the soles of her shoes with a special sharp knife which she kept for the purpose.

'What does Saul do?'

'Never asked him.' Jessamy giggled. 'Probably better not to know!'

The opening ballet of the evening was *Sylphides*, followed by *Spring Sonata*; then came the interval and *Tam O'Shanter* followed by *Faune* and ending up with *Tarantella*. Ginny, predictably, grumbled that Jessamy had not only been given one of the leads, *purely and simply* because of who her parents were, but had even bagged the best spot for herself.

'How *does* she manage it?' wondered Lorraine.

109

Jessamy did her best to take no notice of them. Karen was still indignant on her behalf over the incident of the note which had disappeared from her locker door, but the way Jessamy saw it, rivalry led to jealousy and jealousy led to acts of spite and you just had to rise above them.

Not being on until the end of the evening, Jessamy needn't actually have arrived at the theatre until later, but it seemed an act of solidarity to come in with the others and in any case she had promised Karen that she would give her a crit.

'And you will be *honest*? And then I will be with you.'

While *Sylphides* was on they stayed in the dressing room, Jessamy industriously sewing ribbons on to point shoes (it was not that she was nervous, she told herself; just that it was better to be occupied), Karen sitting scrunched up in a corner, clutching her mascot to her chest. The mascot was one of Saul's old shoes that Jessamy had begged for her: grey, grubby and worn; an object decidedly repellent, if you asked Jessamy, but Karen swore she couldn't go on and dance if she didn't know that it was there, waiting for her in the wings.

Before the curtain came down on *Sylphides* Karen heaved a deep trembly sigh and scrambled to her feet.

'*Buena suerte!*' whispered Jessamy.

Karen gave her an ashen smile. At the door, she turned.

'You will come and watch?'

''Course I will!'

Jessamy put her sewing away (she hated sewing: she could never do it as neatly as Karen) and made her way down to the wings. *Spring Sonata* was a beautiful filigree of a ballet, which might almost have been written for Karen with her precise and delicate style of dancing. She was partnered by John McDonald, who was good, thought Jessamy, judiciously, but not in the same class as Karen.

It was strange how a person so small and meek and – yes, *insignificant*, when set beside someone as flamboyant as, for example, Ginny, with her flaming red hair and green eyes – it was strange how that person could be transformed on stage into a totally other being. No one would ever have guessed that only half an hour before she had been curled up in a corner cuddling an old ballet shoe for comfort and looking as if she might be sick at any moment. Could this vital, darting creature really be the same Karen?

Jessamy watched, with admiration and wonder, as Karen spun on legs of crystal, quivered for a moment, dragonfly-like, then with a flash of cut glass, straight as an arrow, launched herself into a fish dive, holding the pose, arms outstretched, a radiant smile on the face which but a short while since had been pinched and drawn in apprehensive agony. Standing in the wings, Jessamy burst into spontaneous applause, along with the rest of the audience.

'Was it all right?' whispered Karen, as she came off.

'Ace!'

It was so good to be able to say it, and mean it, and feel nothing but a golden glow of warmth and generosity. No more envy, no more worry. Jessamy could accept, now, that of the two of them it was Karen who was destined to be the ballet dancer. Jessamy had other furrows to plough!

In the meanwhile, Mum and Dad were out there and she had to show them what she could do. Jessamy Hart might give up the ballet, but nobody, for one moment, must ever be allowed to think that the ballet had given up her!

Tam and *Faune* both went well – Ginny was on form and received a round of applause – which simply reinforced Jessamy's belief that saying a good dress rehearsal meant a bad performance was pure superstition. It didn't mean a thing. Not a thing, thought Jessamy, making her way back down to the stage for *Tarantella*.

Tarantella was a showpiece – 'All technique and no substance,' sneered Ginny, who was very well aware that her own technique was every bit as strong as Jessamy's. Jessamy herself wasn't quite sure why she should have been chosen to dance the lead in preference to her rival. Maybe just the luck of the draw, though Karen, fiercely loyal, said it was because Jessamy had a bright and sunny personality and Ginny had a mean and sour one.

'Carabosse, that's what she ought to dance!'

Ginny was waiting in the wings as Jessamy prepared for her first entry.

'I wanted to warn you,' she said, 'there's a filthy great nail sticking up right where you have to do your variation.'

112

'Nail?' How could there be a nail? There hadn't been one at rehearsal!

'Don't ask me.' Ginny shrugged. 'I just thought I ought to warn you.'

Jessamy peered out, across the stage. 'I can't see any nail!'

'Over there.' Ginny jerked her head, swivelling Jessamy round to point in the right direction. Jessamy screwed up her eyes. She still couldn't see anything.

'Just watch when you're doing those *fouettés* . . . it could be lethal.'

'Yes, I will. Thanks for telling me.' Jessamy said it awkwardly. Maybe Ginny wasn't so bad, after all. It wasn't everyone who would be that generous with a rival.

Jessamy's variation, with the *fouettés*, came ten minutes into the ballet – and for the entire ten minutes she was obsessed with the thought of a large rusty nail ripping into her feet. Every time she approached that area of the stage her eyes scanned the ground, apprehensively seeking it.

'What's the problem?' hissed Nicky Scott, who was partnering her.

'Nail,' mouthed Jessamy.

'Where?'

'Somewhere! Over there.'

So then Nicky was apprehensive, too, and that made a pair of them, which was even worse than just Jessamy on her own.

The variation loomed up. Deliberately, Jessamy positioned herself as far away as she reasonably

113

could from the spot where she'd danced at rehearsal. That threw her, for a start. The perspective was different, the stage felt different, she was nearer to the other dancers than she ought to be.

She started on the *fouettés*; twenty-six, in all. Not as many as in *Swan Lake*, where there are thirty-two, but a challenge none the less. Madam had said, 'Technique is not an end in itself, Jessamy. No one expects you to conquer Mount Everest at the first attempt. If you can only manage half of them –'

But she could manage them all! She had done so at rehearsal, quite easily. Seventeen, eighteen –

Where was that nail?

Nineteen, twenty –

Was that it, over there?

Twenty-one, twen –

– ty-two, and she found herself slipping. Felt her legs begin to travel forward . . . towards the nail! In terror she tried to pull away, hit a ridge on the stage, lost her balance and promptly catapulted over on to her back, with her legs in the air, her eyes staring up at the flies.

She was on her feet in an instant, but the damage had been done. She turned, and walked upstage with trembling limbs. Maggot, who was waiting with the others for the music to draw them back into the ballet, grimaced fiercely at her.

'Just keep going!' hissed Maggot.

Yes; that was what one had to do. Disaster might strike, but one had to keep going.

Determinedly, Jessamy spun round, flashed a big cheeky beam at the audience and launched herself, with as much verve as she could muster, into what remained of her variation. To her astonishment, a huge outburst of handclapping filled the hall. She even heard people cheering. Anyone would think she had successfully completed some feat of technical brilliance rather than fallen flat on her back and disgraced herself!

'There was no disgrace,' Belinda Tarrant said afterwards. 'It can happen to anyone. You picked yourself up and carried on; that was the main thing.'

Maggot and Karen wanted to know whether she was going to report Ginny to Miss Fane, or even to Madam, for they had all three combed every centimetre of the stage and needless to say not a trace of a nail could be found.

'There never was any nail!' declared Maggot.

'No.' Jessamy accepted it, ruefully. She had fallen for one of the oldest tricks in the book – and reacted just as Ginny had hoped she would.

'But it backfired,' said Karen, ''cause everyone thought you were wonderful. I was out there, and I saw, and when you turned round and grinned I heard a woman say "She's got spirit, I'll give her that." And they were *all* on your side.'

'Yes, but I was such an idiot!' groaned Jessamy. 'Fancy believing her!'

'I think you should tell Miss Fane,' urged Maggot, but Jessamy shook her head.

'I'll know better next time ... she's not playing any more tricks on me!'

8

'A real hotel!' gloated Maggot.

'Jessamy and I have got our own bathroom!' There was wonderment in Karen's voice.

'So've we,' said Nella. 'We've got a hair-dryer in ours. Have you got a hair-dryer?'

'Yes, and soap and shampoo and bath oil and *everything*. There's even a trouser press,' said Karen.

'And all the little bits for making tea and coffee.' Maggot giggled, excitedly. 'We could lie in bed with a drink and watch television!'

'The television is *enormous*,' said Karen.

Jessamy listened, trying not to feel superior, as the three of them exulted over the various miracles to be encountered in a hotel bedroom. Jessamy had been on tour with her parents, she had been for holidays abroad, she had stayed in hotels far grander than this one. But even she couldn't deny that it was fun, being there on their own – well, Miss Fane had come with them, of course, and Miss Eldon, to lend a hand, but once they had shut their bedroom door they could do whatever they liked. Sit up right through the night watching films, if that was what they wanted. Not that we would, thought Jessamy, virtuously; not with performances coming up.

Their first performance was scheduled for tomorrow afternoon, their second for tomorrow evening. They also, as usual, had class with Miss Fane in the morning. There had already been a run-through on stage; now they were back at the hotel, congregating in the dining room for the evening meal.

'My!' said Ginny, walking past their table with Lorraine in tow. 'I'm surprised to find you here . . . couldn't they afford anything more classy? After all, you are the *stars*.'

Jessamy smiled. She had had just about enough of Ginny.

'We could have gone to the Royal Crescent,' she said. The Royal Crescent was where Mum and Dad had been going to stay if they had come down to Bath. 'But we preferred to pig it with the rest of you. Didn't we?' She referred across the table to Karen. 'It seemed more . . . democratic.'

Ginny's lip curled. 'How *frightfully* decent of you.'

'Well, I thought it was,' agreed Jessamy. 'I mean, we only have one bathroom between us, and one television set – '

'And one trouser press,' added Karen, with a rare flash of wit.

'And one trouser press,' said Jessamy. 'It is not quite what one is accustomed to, but I daresay we shall manage.'

Ginny flared her nostrils and swished her hair as she marched off across the room (to a table as far away from Jessamy's as she could possibly get).

'Now she'll really have it in for you,' said Maggot.

Jessamy tossed her head. 'See if I care!'

After dinner, Miss Fane had said they could go

117

into town if they wanted, but they were to be back at the hotel no later than nine – 'Which doesn't properly give one time to do *anything*!' complained Jessamy. But Karen didn't want to do anything, and Maggot said there was something she wanted to watch on television, and Nella, after humming and hawing, decided that perhaps it might be wisest just to spend the evening relaxing.

'Somebody said the critics might be there.'

'You can't let your life be ruled by *critics*,' said Jessamy; but in the end she trailed back upstairs with the rest of them. 'I suppose I could always prepare some more shoes.'

Jessamy hated preparing shoes. Karen always had at least half a dozen pairs all stitched and scraped and broken in ready for use. Karen's shoes were a byword: state of the art. She had recently started unpicking the back seams and taking in neat little tucks so that they fitted her feet like pairs of gloves. Jessamy could only watch and marvel. Such industry! Such patience! She bet Spanish dancers didn't have to go to all that trouble.

'I'm *bored*,' said Jessamy. She sprang towards the television set and began clicking her way round the channels. Karen, who was sitting cross-legged on her bed flipping through the Festival brochure that had been left in their room, suddenly gave a blood-curdling shriek.

'What's the matter?' Jessamy jumped round in a panic. 'What is it? What's wrong?'

'Jessamy – *look*!' Karen held out the brochure.

118

With quivering finger, she pointed to the top of the page.

'*Students of the City Ballet Company –*'

'No! The next bit!'

'*Carlos Miguel y sus Compañeros* – is *that* all? I wish you wouldn't do things like that,' grumbled Jessamy. 'You nearly gave me a heart attack.'

'But Jessamy, they're here! In the Festival!'

'Yes, and they're appearing the same day we are. So you won't be able to go and watch.'

'No, but they're *here*,' gloated Karen. 'Jessamy –' she sprang up from the bed. 'If we went out for a walk we might see them!'

Jessamy shook her head. 'It's too late. It's nearly nine o'clock. Miss Fane'd have a fit if we went out now.'

'We could get up early tomorrow morning,' pleaded Karen.

'To do what?'

'See if we can see them!'

'See them where? There's about nine hundred hotels in this town! And anyway, they'd probably still be in bed. I bet they don't have to be back in their rooms by nine o'clock!'

Karen's mouth puckered. It was what Jessamy called her stubborn-as-a-mule expression.

'There must be *some* way we can find out where they're staying.'

Jessamy considered the matter. 'I suppose you could always try ringing the Festival box office and saying you're a friend of Paco Gonzalez and you want to get in touch with him.'

119

'*Me*?' Karen scrambled back, nervously, on to the bed.

'Well, you're the one who wants to know.'

'Oh, Jessamy! You know I'm no good at that sort of thing!'

'Got to be brave,' said Jessamy, 'if you want to get anywhere. But anyway, I don't expect they'd tell you. I mean, for all they know you could just be some besotted fan. Which of course you are,' said Jessamy.

Karen hung her head. Her hair, loose for once, and very nearly back to its original bright flaxen, slipped forward like a silken waterfall to hide her cheeks.

'I can't bear it if he's in the same town and I can't see him!'

'Oh, look, for heaven's sake,' said Jessamy, taking pity on her. 'If it means that much, I'll find out.'

'Will you?' Karen looked at her with shining eyes. 'Will you really? How?'

'I have my ways,' said Jessamy.

She would ask Saul, after the show tomorrow night. The box office could hardly think *he* was a besotted fan.

As it happened, Jessamy didn't have to ask Saul: she found out all by herself. People were gathering in the hotel foyer next morning, waiting for the cabs which were to ferry them to the theatre. Jessamy and Karen were two of the first down. Karen, being Karen, had meekly parked herself on a sofa next to a potted plant: Jessamy, being Jessamy, had wandered over to have a chat with the receptionist.

'Do you ever get any celebrities staying here?' said Jessamy.

'I thought you were celebrities!' joked the receptionist.

'We might be,' said Jessamy, 'some day.'

'But not just yet?'

'We haven't performed yet,' said Jessamy. 'I suppose, after this evening, we could be *mini* celebrities.'

'Oh, well, that'll do! That'll count. We've got all your signatures here in the book ... I expect by this time tomorrow I'll be putting them up for auction!'

'But what about real celebrities?' persisted Jessamy. 'Do you ever get any of those?'

'We've got the Spanish ballet.'

'Carlos Miguel?' Heavens, thought Jessamy. What a piece of luck! Wait till Karen hears this!

'There you are.' The receptionist flipped back a page in the visitors' book. She pointed, with a long red fingernail.

Jessamy's eye leapt at once to a signature she recognised: Paco Gonzalez.

'If I asked you which rooms they were staying in,' she said, 'would you tell me?'

'What do you think?' said the receptionist.

Jessamy wrinkled her nose. 'I suppose not.'

'You suppose quite correctly.'

'But I don't see why not,' said Jessamy.

'Because (a) I can't afford to lose my job, and (b) you're just being nosy!'

'Oh, all right,' said Jessamy. She grinned. 'I expect we'll see them around!'

The taxis had arrived and Miss Fane was beckoning impatiently to her to 'Come along, Jessamy, and don't keep people waiting!' Jessamy bounced across the foyer and squeezed into a cab with Karen, Maggot and Nella, and oh, bother, Miss Fane as well! She couldn't tell Karen the good news in front of Miss Fane. In fact she was in two minds whether to tell Karen the good news at all. It would only send her into a flap and take her mind off the performance. Jessamy decided that it could wait until afterwards, when they were alone together.

Something else she hadn't yet broken to Karen was that Saul and Ken were going to be in tonight's audience. That, too, she had been intending to keep for afterwards, but Karen found out anyway for amongst the many telegrams they received from people such as Mum and Dad, and Karen's gran, and Susan and Sheela and even Jack and the Bottler, whom she wouldn't have expected to remember, there were two from Saul and Ken.

One was for Jessamy. The other was for Karen. The one for Jessamy said, *Knock 'em for six! See you after the show. Love Saul & Ken.*

The one for Karen said, *All the best for this evening. Love Ken & Saul.*

'Isn't that nice?' beamed Jessamy. 'Mine says Saul and Ken and yours says Ken and Saul.'

'Let's have a read of yours,' said Karen.

'Oh, well, it's just the same as yours, really,' said Jessamy, hastily scrumpling it into a ball.

'Then why are you hiding it from me? Jessamy!' Karen made a snatch. 'Let's see!'

'Yes, we all want to see.' Maggot eyed Jessamy,

sternly. 'You're supposed to *display* your telegrams, not scrunch them up like that.'

'What does it say?' said Nella. She peered at it over Karen's shoulder and squeaked. '*See you after the show*? Does that mean he's going to be out there? He's going to be watching us? Jessamy! Why didn't you say?'

''Cause I didn't want to cause a riot,' said Jessamy.

'*Jessamy*.' Karen was looking at her with eyes full of reproach. 'How could you? You were going to keep it from me!'

'Keep it from all of us,' said Maggot.

Jessamy shrugged. 'Well, if you think you can handle it – ' She just hadn't wanted Karen going to pieces. She suffered enough from nerves as it was.

'It's worse than having Madam out there!' moaned Nella.

'No, it's not.' Jessamy said it very firmly. They would all be going to pieces if she weren't careful. 'Saul's just coming to enjoy himself. He's not going to march round afterwards and tear everyone to pieces.'

'No, he'll just make mental notes that there are certain people he doesn't ever, ever want to dance with!'

'It's not up to him who he dances with. He doesn't run the Company.'

'Want to bet?' murmured Ginny; and of course it was perfectly true that if there were anyone Saul violently objected to partnering, Madam probably wouldn't try to force him.

Lorraine, dragging on her tights, said, 'She's probably sent him along as a spy.'

'She has not!' retorted Jessamy. 'He's coming because he wants to.'

'Wants to see his little sister,' crooned Ginny. 'How sweet!'

'Well, it is,' said Maggot, 'so you can just shut up, Ginny Alexander!'

Jessamy leaned across to Karen. 'You're not going to freak,' she whispered, 'are you?'

Karen gave her a wobbly sort of smile. 'Hope not.'

'Don't hope! *Promise*.'

'All right.' Karen swallowed. 'I promise!'

Saturday 16 July
Definitely the most amazing and incredible day of my ENTIRE LIFE!!!

Oh, and it started so badly! Well, the evening did, and everyone knows it's the evening performance that counts because that's when all the really important people come. All the critics, for instance, and Saul.

Jessamy was so mean, she wasn't going to tell me that Saul was out front! She said it was because she didn't want me going to pieces, and maybe she was right because it did make me nervous, but they sent us telegrams, him and Ken, and that's how I discovered, and of course everyone else discovered as well, and so then we were all nervous, except Jessamy who hardly ever is, and Ginny who doesn't have any feelings.

I have come to the conclusion that Ginny is a truly horrible person. I said to Jessamy while we were sit-

124

ting in the dressing room, 'If she tries telling you there are any nails in the stage, just don't take any notice of her,' and Jessamy said she wouldn't, she said she'd learnt her lesson and that she was stupid ever to have believed her in the first place. And then she added, 'But you'd better watch out because she's angry as a hornet about not getting to dance a lead, and you know you're so innocent she could play any trick she liked on you.'

I honestly didn't think she would, not after what she did to Jessamy, but I said I'd be on my guard, and I was during the afternoon performance, but then nothing happened and Ginny was really nice and said how well I'd danced and how she always liked to watch me and so I got lulled (that is what Jessamy says) and forgot all about her being angry as a hornet with the result that the evening performance was very nearly a DISASTER. This was for two reasons, one of which had nothing to do with Ginny, being a complete accident, though the other I am convinced was down to her, and so are Jessamy and Maggot.

What happened was I lost my lucky mascot! My ballet shoe that Jessamy got for me from Saul and which I cannot dance without. I know it is silly and superstitious but lots of people have them including some dancers that are quite famous. I left it on my dressing table while I went down to watch the opening of Sylphides, which I adore, and when I went back it had disappeared! I was going almost frantic and everyone was helping look for it, including Ginny, and I just couldn't think where it might have gone. People kept saying things like 'Maybe you took it with you when you went to the loo?' or 'Maybe you dropped it somewhere?' or 'Are you really sure you had it?' until I began to think I was going mad because I knew that I'd left it in the dressing room.

And then right at the last minute, literally at the last minute, when I was waiting to go on and was totally and utterly convinced that something awful was going to happen, Jessamy appeared, waving it at me! She told me afterwards that she'd suddenly thought of up-ending the waste paper basket, even though it wasn't anywhere near my dressing table, and there it was, my mascot, hidden under a pile of screwed up tissue paper.

Jessamy said the paper had obviously been put there on purpose to cover it up, and Maggot says she remembers Ginny having something wrapped in tissue paper, which I know is not evidence, strictly speaking, but it's a very strange coincidence is all one can say – especially as the waste paper basket was over Ginny's side of the dressing room and there is just no way that Saul's shoe could have got into it unless someone had deliberately put it there, and who else would do such a mean thing? I don't think Lorraine would, even though she is Ginny's friend. I hate being suspicious of people but am afraid Jessamy is right and that not everybody in ballet is nice.

Anyway, the one good thing about me being so worried over not having my mascot was that it took my mind off other things, just a tiny bit. I didn't actually forget that Saul was out there, but I kept thinking, 'If only I had my mascot everything would be all right!' and then I did have it, and everything was, at least for most of the time.

I'd just got to the part where I have to do my final variation when to my utter astonishment and amazement I saw John go walking off stage! He isn't supposed to go off stage! He is supposed to be there, to step in and support me! I thought at first he'd had a brainstorm and would come back as soon as he realised what he'd done, but then to my horror I looked off into the wings and there he was, rolling about on the floor in obvious agony, clutching at one of his legs. I didn't have time to feel worried that he may have suffered a terrible injury (I think it's something to do with a ligament, or maybe a muscle, I'm not sure), I was just petrified thinking how I was going to get through the rest of my variation without anyone to support me. I know that sounds selfish but it is truly terrifying to be left on stage without any partner and wondering all the time what you are going to do when you get to the bits that you can't manage on your own. How can you do a fish dive without anyone to catch you???

I was about half way through the variation, the part where I have to walk to the back of the stage and then go pirouetting down, which is where John was supposed to come in to support me, and I was really beginning to panic, because I could do the pirouettes all right but what was going to happen after that? So I got to the back of the stage and I was shaking all over like a jelly and I started on the pirouettes and with the very first turn I just couldn't believe what I was seeing because there, all of a sudden, was Saul!

I thought for a moment he was a mirage and that I was imagining it, but I wasn't, it was really him, solid flesh and blood, waiting to take over where poor John had had to leave off. I was so relieved I couldn't immediately grasp how altogether incredible it was. It only hit me later. I WAS DANCING WITH SAUL!

He told us afterwards that he'd guessed immediately when John made his hasty exit that there must be something wrong and so he'd gone rushing backstage to see if he could help and found John thrashing about on the floor and everyone tearing their hair out wondering what to do, because we didn't have any understudies. It was fortunate Saul was the one who'd premiered the ballet and thus knew it inside out. It was also fortunate, thank goodness, that I was able to carry on by myself just for those few minutes otherwise I can't imagine what would have happened. As it was, Saul said he just tore John's costume off him and dived into it (lucky it fitted!) and arrived on stage in the nick of time. That must be one of the fastest costume changes on record!

Now I'm back in our hotel room with Jessamy, who says she is jealous because I got to dance with Saul before she did and now she probably never will. I don't think she is really jealous because Jessamy isn't like that and also she danced so well herself. Everyone was saying how brilliant she was. But in any case I can't feel guilty about dancing with Saul because I am just too deliriously happy! Jessamy says that I have fulfilled my heart's desire, and it is true that I have fulfilled one of my heart's desires. (In a minute I am going to lie down and re-live it all, step by step, and

*this time I will be able to relax and enjoy it properly
which I couldn't while it was happening on account of
not quite being able to believe that it was happening.)*

*My other heart's desire may not ever be fulfilled
because I can't see there is any chance that I could
dance with Paco, and bother! I have just remembered
that in all the excitement I forgot to ask Jessamy
whether she had discovered where he is staying, which
she promised she was going to do. She is asleep and
I don't like to wake her up. I shall ask her in the
morning.*

9

It was nearly midnight when Jessamy was woken by the sound of voices raised in anger in the corridor outside. She lay for a second, listening. Spanish? Were they talking Spanish?

Abruptly, she threw back the bedclothes and went pattering across to the door. As she did so, Karen sat up in bed and whispered, 'What is it?'

'Sh!' Jessamy pressed her ear to the door crack. The voices were receding slightly, moving away down the corridor. Mostly all she could hear was an angry stream of sound, but the odd one or two words she managed to pick out were definitely Spanish.

Karen came tiptoeing across to join her.

'What's happening?'

'I think they're having a row!'

'Who?'

'I forgot to tell you,' whispered Jessamy. In all the drama of last night, with John going and injuring himself and Saul taking over and everyone giving him and Karen a standing ovation, it had quite slipped her memory. 'They're staying here ... in the hotel!'

Karen's mouth gaped open. '*Paco*?'

'All of them. I saw their names in the book.' Jessamy turned and snatched up her dressing gown.

'What are you doing?' squeaked Karen.

'Going to have a look.'

'But Jessa- '

'Sh!'

Jessamy eased the door open and slid out into the corridor. She was just in time to see Paco and his father, gesticulating furiously, jabbing their fingers into the air and into each other, disappear round the corner at the far end. Silent as a shadow, she slipped after them.

'*Jessamy*!'

Karen flew behind her, barefooted, struggling into her dressing gown. Jessamy pointed, and placed a warning finger on her lips.

Hugging the wall, they crept soundlessly in pursuit of their quarry. At the end of the corridor, they paused. The voices could still be heard, but muffled. Jessamy risked a quick glance round the corner: the corridor was empty. The voices, now, were coming from behind a closed door. Boldly, Jessamy stole up to it. Karen, terrified yet unable to resist, stole after her.

From inside the room came more of the angry shouting. Jessamy giggled.

'That's rude,' she said.

She giggled again.

'That's even more rude!'

How did Jessamy know all these rude words? wondered Karen. From Marisol, presumably; they certainly weren't in the Spanish phrase book that Karen had borrowed from the library.

Without any warning the door was flung open and

131

Paco came striding out. Karen and Jessamy had no time to hide themselves, but fortunately he was in too much of a rage to notice them.

'*Tu madre*!' he shouted; and sent a contemptuous one-fingered gesture winging over his shoulder as he went stalking off down the corridor.

Jessamy and Karen bundled themselves back round the corner and scampered for the safety of their own room.

'Oh!' Jessamy, giggling, closed the door behind them. 'That was the rudest of all!'

'What, what he said?'

'*Tu madre*!' Jessamy imitated Paco's contemptuous gesture.

Karen was puzzled. 'All it means is "your mother".'

'I don't care; it's rude. Marisol told me. It's swearing.'

Karen gnawed at her lip. She had to admit, the way he had shouted it, defiantly, over his shoulder, it had certainly sounded like swearing.

'It's no use trying to make a saint out of him,' said Jessamy. 'Dancers aren't ever saints. You want to hear some of the things Saul and Colleen shout at each other! I remember once this reporter came to interview them and they asked the stage manager if Saul and Colleen were in love and the stage manager said well, perhaps not in *love*, exactly, and the reporter said "But is there any romantic attachment?" and the stage manager said well, not so much romantic as – um – *spiritual*, perhaps, and then when they got to Colleen's dressing room – ' Jessamy

132

chuckled, happily – 'all they could hear was the sound of her and Saul yelling at each other! 'Cause you know,' said Jessamy, 'they can't stand each other. Not in real life. I think that's really funny,' said Jessamy. 'Having this wonderful spiritual relationship and spitting all these hideous and horrible insults at each other!'

Karen was looking at her doubtfully. 'Were you actually there?'

'Well, no, I wasn't actually *there*. Someone told me.'

'It's just that gossip isn't always true,' said Karen.

'Oh – ' Jessamy pulled a face. 'You simply don't want to believe anything bad about Saul! You ask him . . . I bet he'll remember! 'Cause then they went and did this article saying how they fought like cat and dog and Colleen was absolutely furious.'

'How do you *know*?' Karen said it earnestly.

''Cause I read the article!'

'But how do you know about Colleen being furious?'

''Cause she would be! She likes everyone to think she's all sweet and lovely.'

'Yes, but – '

'*Tu madre*!' said Jessamy, copying Paco's gesture. She flounced herself back under the bedclothes. Why did Karen always have to take everything so *seriously*?

There was silence for a few minutes, then Karen's voice spoke, apologetically, into the darkness.

'Jessamy?'

'Mm?'

133

'Do you think we might see them tomorrow morning?'

Jessamy bounced over on to her side. 'Might do. At breakfast.'

''Cause we don't have to get up *terribly* early. Do we? Not as early as everyone else.'

Karen and Jessamy had been given special permission to travel back to London with Saul and Ken, on the train. All the others, with Miss Fane and Miss Eldon, were going back the way they had come, by coach. Miss Fane had said, 'Well, I suppose, Jessamy, as he's your brother ... but what about your train fares?' She had glanced at Karen as she spoke. Everybody knew that Karen was on a scholarship and that her gran didn't have much money.

'Oh,' Jessamy had said, carelessly, 'Saul will see to that.'

Miss Fane had raised both her eyebrows. 'What a very nice brother he must be,' she said.

He was, thought Jessamy. He was the nicest brother a person could have. And she was really glad he wasn't ever going to get married and have babies, like Jack and the Bottler, because that meant she would always be someone special to him.

Jessamy hugged herself. Life was beginning to work out really well. If she could just manage to convince Mum and Dad ...

'Jessamy,' said Karen, 'are you *sure* that it's swearing?'

'Positive,' said Jessamy. 'Marisol said that I wasn't ever to say it.'

Karen sighed.

134

'You might as well face it,' said Jessamy. 'His language is not what your gran would approve of.' She giggled. 'Perhaps you oughtn't to see him again.'

'Oh, *Jessamy*!' wailed Karen.

They were up next morning at half past eight, which seemed very luxurious indeed to people used to waking at six-thirty every day for school. By the time they arrived in the dining room, the others were finished and trailing back upstairs to collect their bags and suitcases.

'You're so lucky,' sighed Nella, who always got sick in coaches even when she'd stuffed herself with travel sickness pills. 'I wish I could go back by train.'

'You mean,' said Maggot, bluntly, 'you wish you could go back with Saul.'

'Oh, well, yes! That, too,' agreed Nella. 'Except I wouldn't dare talk to him!'

'That's right, you'd just sit there gobbling like a half-witted goldfish.'

'I don't know why everyone is so terrified of him,' said Jessamy. 'He's really quite nice.' She turned to Karen. 'Isn't he?'

Karen nodded, blissfully.

'He may be quite nice,' said Maggot, 'but he's still a *star*.'

'And we are nobodies, I suppose,' said Nella, wistfully, 'he didn't say anything? About the performances?'

'Not last night 'cause we were too busy talking.'

Even Jessamy could be diplomatic enough to tell a white lie upon occasion. She had said to Saul, 'What did you think of Maggot and Nella?' and

Saul had said, 'Which ones were they?' And when Jessamy had pointed them out on the programme to remind him, he had grimaced slightly and said, 'Good little dancers, but nothing special ... I'm afraid the only ones who really stood out were you and Karen and that girl with the red hair.'

Ginny. Jessamy pulled down the corners of her mouth. She wasn't going to report *that*!

'I expect there might be a write-up on Monday,' she said, comfortingly. 'Saul said Eric Lauder was there.'

'Goodness! Help!'

'Does Saul know Eric Lauder?'

'Yes, but he doesn't butter him up,' said Jessamy. There were some dancers who spent their lives wining and dining the critics; Saul had never been one of those. What Saul always said was, 'It's a good idea to be on friendly terms, but I don't believe in crawling.'

Jessamy didn't believe in crawling, either. On the other hand, even if they were complete *urgs* (utterly repulsive and gross) it didn't do to offend them. You had to tread a fine line.

Karen, of course, didn't tread any sort of line, being totally innocent and unaware, but Jessamy bet she got a rave from Eric Lauder, all the same!

The others went off to their coach, leaving Jessamy and Karen alone in the dining room. They sat for as long as they could, but not a single dancer from Carlos Miguel's company appeared. Jessamy guessed they had all gone to bed late and that even half past eight was too early for them. Or maybe, another idea

136

struck her: 'Maybe they've all gone to mass!' she said, brightly. 'They're bound to be Catholics, being Spanish.'

Needless to say, Karen instantly wanted to go rushing out to find the nearest Catholic church. It was only fear of incurring Saul's displeasure that stopped her.

'I said we'd be with them by ten o'clock at the very latest,' said Jessamy, sternly. 'We haven't got time to go maundering about looking for churches.'

They had another creep along the corridor and listened hopefully for a few seconds outside Carlos Miguel's room, but all was silent and Karen reluctantly allowed herself to be dragged off.

'Don't forget you'll be seeing him again in Croydon,' urged Jessamy.

But it wasn't the same, thought Karen. It wasn't the same as seeing him in the hotel.

After a slow, lazy stroll through Bath, gazing at the Pump Room and the Assembly Rooms, at the Abbey and the Royal Crescent, they had lunch in a pub, sitting outside in the garden, and caught the afternoon train back to London. Saul and Ken sat together, Karen and Jessamy sat opposite. After a few minutes Karen put her mouth to Jessamy's ear and whispered rather urgently.

'The loo?' said Jessamy. 'It'll be near the first class.' Loos were always near the first class so that people who had paid a lot of money didn't have to walk too far. 'Down that way, I should think.'

Karen set off, looking self-conscious. So silly, thought Jessamy, who had never been self-conscious in her life. After all, everyone had to go to the loo. Even the Queen. Even Saul. Even Paco Gonzalez.

A few minutes later, Karen reappeared. Her cheeks were bright beetroot, but with excitement, this time, not embarrassment. She flung herself down next to Jessamy.

'Guess what!'

'What?'

'He's on the train!'

'Oh, wow!' cried Jessamy. She leaned across to Saul and Ken. 'Did you hear that? He's on the train!'

'Who is?' said Ken, politely.

'Paco!' Jessamy fell back against Karen in a mock swoon. 'Paco Gonzalez! *Viva España! Hasta la vista! Qué hora es*?'

'Ten minutes past three,' said Saul.

Jessamy blinked. 'Pardon?'

'I thought you were asking what the time was.'

'Was I? Oh, well, I didn't mean to. I meant to explain that there was a Gorgeous Being on the train. Where is he?' she demanded of Karen.

Karen, looking like nothing so much as a big red radish, muttered, 'In the next compartment.'

'In the next compartment!' Jessamy sprang up. '*Vamos a ver*!'

'Oh, Jessamy, no!'

'Why not? You went and looked!'

'Yes, but that was by accident.'

'So will this be! Totally by accident!' Jessamy made a snatch at Saul's hand. 'Come! Come and have a look!'

'Why do I want to come and have a look?'

"Cause you'll like him ... he's v-e-r-y s-e-x-y!'

Jessamy dashed off up the carriage, dragging Saul behind her.

'Irrepressible,' murmured Ken. 'I think that's the word.'

When they came back they were carrying cans of drink and packets of biscuits.

'See?' said Jessamy. 'We didn't draw attention to ourselves. And he *is* sexy, isn't he?'

'Oh, yes,' said Saul. 'Very hunky!'

A few minutes later, 'Shall we go and talk to him?' suggested Jessamy, having finished her orange juice and her packet of biscuits and already in search of something else to while away the time. 'Shall we go and introduce ourselves?'

'No!' Karen yelped it, in horror.

'*I* could go and introduce myself.'

'Jessamy, no!' Karen caught at her hand, beseechingly.

'Why not? Why shouldn't I?'

'Because Karen doesn't want you to,' said Saul. 'You just keep out of it. This is her passion, not yours.'

'So I suppose I can just go to the *loo*?' said Jessamy. She was never able to keep still for very long on train journeys. 'I'll go and spy on him and tell you what he's doing ... and I won't say a word, I promise!'

When she and Saul had passed through the carriage the first time, Paco had been sitting next to Maria Rojas but leaning forward engaged in a heated exchange of words with Carlos Miguel. He hadn't

139

noticed Saul and Jessamy. This time, he was standing by the open window at the end of the compartment, scowling as he drank something out of a can. He didn't look particularly approachable; in fact, thought Jessamy, he looked positively forbidding. Obviously simmering about something.

She said, 'Excuse me' (saying excuse me could hardly be classed as talking) and he glanced at her briefly with smouldering black eyes in which, just for a second, there seemed to be a flicker of recognition, and then stepped aside to let her pass.

Jessamy said, '*Muchas gracias!*' (you had to be polite) and walked on quickly before she could be tempted to say more. She would have liked to say more for there were things she would have liked to ask him; but a promise was a promise and Jessamy was nothing if not honourable. Fortunately, on the way back, he had been joined by his cousin, Pepe Ruiz, and they were talking in very fast incomprehensible Spanish, with their heads close together, so that Jessamy couldn't have said anything anyway, which was just as well, for honourable though she might be Jessamy was someone who found it very difficult to keep quiet.

'What was he doing?' whispered Karen, as Jessamy returned.

'Brooding,' said Jessamy. 'Probably deciding to stick a knife in someone. I think he and Carlos Miguel must have had another row. Honestly, you should have heard them last night!' she said to Saul. 'Their language was simply frightful. Almost as bad as the things you and Colleen say to each other.'

'Colleen and I,' said Saul, 'are frigidly polite.'

'Except when you're swearing,' said Jessamy, for Karen's benefit.

They had reached the outskirts of London when Karen decided, urgently, that she must go to the loo again.

'That's right,' said Jessamy, kindly. 'Go and have another look.'

Karen blushed, fiercely, but went anyhow. Jessamy shook her head.

'Pathetic!'

'On the contrary,' said Saul, 'it's not in the least pathetic, it's ecstatic and wonderful and I feel extremely sorry for anyone who's never experienced it.'

'Have you ever?' said Jessamy.

'Of course I have!'

'*Really*?' Jessamy opened her eyes very wide. 'You mean you were as dippy as Karen?'

'Every bit!'

'Who were you dippy about?'

'Yes, come on!' said Ken. 'This is interesting . . . who were you dippy about? Spill the beans!'

'Was it a dancer?'

'Not telling you.'

'Someone in the Company?'

'Not telling you.'

'Man or woman?'

'How many more times do I have to say? I'm not telling you!'

'You mean you won't even tell Ken?'

'I might tell Ken, in strictest confidence. But I am

141

certainly –' Saul leaned forward to squash a finger against Jessamy's nose – 'not divulging it to you!'

'Why not?' Jessamy was aggrieved. 'I'm your sister!'

'Sisters don't get to hear everything.'

'So how old were you?'

Saul shrugged. 'Fifteen. Sixteen.'

'*Madre mia*!' said Jessamy. 'I can't imagine it!'

'I know you can't, that's why I'm not going to tell you. Just accept that some of us are more vulnerable than others – and be kind to Karen.'

'I *am* kind to her,' said Jessamy, 'but it's very tiresome . . . she's got it a thousand times worse than she ever had it over you.'

'That's because he's a thousand times more gorgeous than I am.'

'He is not!' Jessamy was indignant.

'Of course he is. He is an Espanish dancer!'

Saul jumped up and snapped his fingers. Jessamy, unable to resist the temptation, jumped up with him.

'Hey! *Ay, ay!*' Saul began clapping his hands, appreciatively, as there in the middle of the empty carriage she danced. Swirling, stamping, back arched, head held high, arms raised, proud and fierce and angular, a far cry indeed from the gentle curves of the ballet. This was a Jessamy Saul had never seen before; a Jessamy of fire and passion, eyes a-blaze, driven by some inner fury.

'*Anda, jaleo, jaleo! Olé! Brava, brava! Excelente!* Where did you learn to do that, little sister? That looked to me like the real thing!'

142

'Oh – ' A rare blush stole over Jessamy's face. 'You know! With Mr Badowski.'

'Badowski taught you *that*?'

'Well – ' Jessamy broke off, in some confusion, as Karen reappeared.

'Taught her what?' said Karen.

'Everything! Don't be so nosy!' Jessamy plumped herself down again on to her seat. 'So what happened? Did you go and check up on him?'

'I just sort of . . . walked past.'

'And swivelled your eyes! *I* know.'

'Anyway, what about you?' said Karen. 'What were you stamping for?'

'She was showing off her Spanish dancing.' Saul regarded Jessamy thoughtfully from under his lashes. 'But then, you've got something to show off about, haven't you? You never learnt that from Alex Badowski!'

Karen looked at Jessamy, wonderingly.

'We've been doing the dances from *Tricorne*,' said Jessamy, 'haven't we?'

Saul laughed, softly. 'Dances from *Tricorne*?' He shook his head. 'No way!'

Jessamy was glad that at that moment the train drew into Paddington station and she was able to busy herself pulling on her jacket and humping her bag down from the rack. Once on the platform Karen's attention was mercifully diverted from her and fixed firmly on Paco, who had jumped out of the train ahead of them and was walking very fast and purposefully towards the barrier. Karen and Jessamy

143

sleuthed him as far as the exit and then lost him when he jumped into a taxi.

'We could always jump into another one and say "Follow that cab!" ' said Jessamy.

Karen just sighed.

'I would,' said Jessamy. 'No bottle, that's your trouble.'

Saul and Ken, refusing to be hurried, strolled in leisurely fashion towards them.

'Well, this has all been very exciting,' said Saul, 'hasn't it?'

'The most exciting thing – ' Karen assured him of it, earnestly – 'was last night when I turned round and saw you standing there on stage.'

'Get away with you!' said Saul. 'How can I hope to compete?' He rattled his heels in passable imitation of a *zapateado*. 'You enjoy it,' he said, 'while it lasts. And don't let my dear little sister put you off . . . she doesn't know what she's missing!'

'Don't worry.' Jessamy said it consolingly as she and Karen made their way down into the underground to catch a tube home. 'You'll be seeing him again in two weeks!'

10

On Monday, in *The Guardian*, there was a write-up by Eric Lauder.

'Here you are,' said Jessamy's dad. 'Read all about it.'

Jessamy snatched eagerly at the paper. Two members of the graduate class and three of the seniors had been singled out for praise. The three seniors were Karen, Jessamy and Ginny – with a kind word reserved for John McDonald, 'an honest and considerate partner in the classical mould'.

Jessamy was described as 'bright and sparky, full of exuberance and charm. A natural, one would say, for Swanhilda or Lisa'. Lisa in *La Fille Mal Gardée*! Right at the top of her dad's hit list! Jessamy shot a worried glance at him across the kitchen table, but her dad only nodded and stuck up a thumb.

'Not bad, eh? Coming from the great Lauder.'

Jessamy smiled, rather weakly, with relief. Bright and sparky . . . exuberance and charm. Yes, she would agree with all those!

Ginny was picked out for the 'metallic brilliance of her technique . . . with a diamond-hard personality to match'. Was that supposed to be good, or not? She read it aloud, to her dad.

'Might be OK if you wanted to write a ballet for an automaton,' he said.

Ha! thought Jessamy. She would tell that to Maggot and Nella; they would appreciate that.

Or perhaps on second thoughts, she wouldn't. They would be bound to ask whether they had been mentioned, and then she would have to admit that they hadn't. Nobody liked to feel that they had failed to make an impression, save under the general heading of 'all-round excellence of students from the City Ballet School'.

It was Karen, as expected, who had received the biggest write-up. Almost half a column! Jessamy let her eye slip quickly down the page, picking out all the important bits.

'... *remember the very first time I saw this dancer ... posed* en arabesque *in the foyer of the Fountain Theatre ... totally oblivious of her surroundings. Thought then – one of these days – star material –* '

And so on and so forth, thought Jessamy, without any rancour. No more the mean little prickles of jealousy; those days were past. Now she could read and be objective, agreeing with all that was said.

'*A dancer of filigree perfection, with a line as pure as swallows in flight, quick, light footwork of needle-point precision, and the seeming fragility of finest silver thread. This is a future Giselle if ever I saw one!*'

Right, thought Jessamy. Eric Lauder was right – and she couldn't wait to show Karen!

Karen, predictably, was thrown into confusion,

obviously eager to wallow, to read and re-read and read yet again, but fearful of seeming to gloat or be insensitive.

'I wish he'd mentioned Maggot and Nella!'

'Yes, instead of Ginny, but Dad says Ginny's the sort who'll always attract attention.'

'I don't think we ought to show them,' said Karen, anxiously, 'do you?'

Jessamy agreed that it might probably be kinder, but when they arrived at school they found that the news had already spread.

'Charm and exuberance!' hooted Nella.

'Filigree perfection!' mocked Maggot.

They were teasing, but not unkindly. They were doing it to cover their own hurt and disappointment. Jessamy understood this and played up to it, valiantly.

'Exuberance just means bouncy,' she said. 'Boing, boing, boing!' And she bounced, Tiggerlike, across the changing room.

'But *charm*,' said Nella.

Jessamy simpered. 'Off the top of a chocolate box!'

It was left to Ginny, as usual, to introduce a sour note.

'It does of course help,' she remarked conversationally to Lorraine, 'if one has a brother who invites critics to his parties.' How had she heard about that? 'As for posing *en arabesque* in the foyer of the Fountain – '

'Anyone is free to do it,' snapped Maggot.

It was true: anyone *was* free to do it. Whether

147

they would have the nerve – or, as in Karen's case, be as blissfully unaware – was another matter. But not everyone, thought Jessamy soberly, had a brother who invited Eric Lauder to his parties. Not everyone had parents who were famous dancers and had known Eric Lauder for over a quarter of a century.

Some of her pleasure began slowly to trickle away. Was that really the only reason Eric Lauder had said she was bright and sparky and full of charm and exuberance? But I am bright and sparky! thought Jessamy. And I am full of exuberance! She didn't know about being charming; no one had ever said that before.

'Oh, Jessamy, of course you are!' cried Karen, when Jessamy finally managed to bring herself to voice her doubts. 'Of course he's not just saying it because of Saul! You've got *loads* of charm. Not p'raps so much in real life,' she added, dashing any pretensions which Jessamy might have been about to have, 'but on stage . . . that bit in *Tarantella* where you kick up your foot and flick your dress and sort of . . . roll your eyes at the audience and give them a little grin – '

'Saucy, Eric Lauder said it was.' Not charming.

'Well, it is,' agreed Karen, 'but it makes everyone smile. And that other bit, where you go skipping off round the stage with your tambourine . . . it's like – like *sunshine*,' said Karen. 'Honestly! You don't want to take any notice of anything Ginny says. You were the one that told *me* that.'

'Yes, I know.' Jessamy heaved a sigh. 'It's just

that although there's lots of advantages, having parents that are famous – '

'And a brother!'

'And a brother, and I wouldn't swop Saul for *any-body*, but it does make it difficult,' said Jessamy, 'trying to decide whether people mean it when they say nice things or whether they just want to cosy up to Mum and Dad.'

'Or Saul.' Karen nodded. 'I can see that it's a problem, but you must know *really* that what he said was true.'

Jessamy supposed that she did, but how much easier if she could strike out on her own! Make conquests in fields where Mum and Dad – and Saul – had never ventured!

'The test will be,' she said, 'whether Madam keeps me on.'

No one could ever accuse Madam of cosying up to anyone. If Madam offered Jessamy a place in the graduate class it would be purely and simply because she thought she was a good dancer.

'I'm sure she will,' said Karen, 'otherwise she wouldn't have chosen you to dance a lead. But is it what you want?'

'It's necessary,' said Jessamy.

Monday 18 July

*... She wouldn't say any more. Just 'It's necessary.'
I don't know what she's up to. All I know is that she's happy, which she wasn't last year, and she doesn't seem bothered so much about losing weight. She even looked in the mirror the other day and giggled and*

said, 'I'm getting boobs!' as if she liked the idea. Not me! I don't ever want to have any.

Tuesday 19 July
Today we finished for the summer. No more classes till September! Well, Jessamy and I will do class together, of course, but it's not the same as being at ballet school. I don't think I could live without dancing.

I am almost certain that I am going to be asked back because Miss Perlman called me into the office this morning and spoke to me about my scholarship and as good as said I'd be offered one for next year, but I daren't count on it till I hear officially.

Miss Fane says we should have our letters by the end of the week!

It is almost as bad as when we were waiting to hear whether we'd got into ballet school originally, though not quite as nerve-racking because as Angie says, at least we've had four years of training and could probably find a place somewhere else, though it wouldn't be the same and you would most likely end up dancing in musicals or night-clubs. That is what Angie thinks she will do. She is going to try and get into a drama school if Madam doesn't ask her back, which she says she knows she won't and she is no doubt right. She is taking it very calmly. I wouldn't!

Wednesday 20 July
I am working in the horrible supermarket again, every evening from five o'clock till seven and eight on Thursdays but no Saturdays, thank goodness. Jessamy

150

is working, too! She has gone back to Markham's but odd hours, what she calls 'shifts', which means sometimes in the morning and sometimes in the evening, except she doesn't have to stay late on Thursdays so she is luckier than me. I don't know why she is working at all. She surely can't enjoy it? She says she needs the money but I can't imagine what for.

No letter yet!

Thursday 21 July
Still no letter.

Friday 22 July
Still no letter. I am getting really nervous!

Saturday 23 July
It came! And I have been asked back and my scholarship has been renewed! Gran is so excited about it, you'd think she'd always wanted to have a dancer for a granddaughter instead of, as once upon a time, being so opposed on account of Granddad wanting me to have an education, which Gran didn't think dancing was. But now she has changed her mind and is going round telling all her friends about me! Oh, I do hope I manage to get into the Company and am given some good roles to dance before Gran is too old to come and see me!

A very strange thing happened today. Jessamy's mum rang up and asked if she could come round and talk to me – about Jessamy!!! She said, 'I'm hoping you can set my mind at rest. I'm a bit worried about her.' Of course I said she could come, because I couldn't really say anything else, though I'm not sure Jessamy would like the thought of me talking to her mum about her.

Anyway this was quite late, about three o'clock, ages after I'd opened my letter. I wanted to ask if Jessamy's had come, and if so what was in it, but I didn't quite like to, but as it happened it was almost the very first thing her mum said. She said, 'It came this morning after Jessamy had left for this absurd job she insists on doing. I haven't opened it, of course, but – ' I could tell that she was itching to! So then she asked me if I knew why Jessamy was doing a job, and I had to confess that I didn't. I said, 'She told me she needed the money,' and this seemed to be absolutely the wrong thing to say because when I said it her mum looked very grim and her lips went into this thin line and she said, 'I see,' in a voice that wasn't cross so much as – I don't know how to explain it. It was like she'd been expecting bad news and I'd just given it to her. She said, 'I feared it might be that.'

She wanted to know if I had any idea what Jessamy needed the money for, but of course I haven't. She's been really secretive the whole term. And then her mum said, 'You don't happen to know where she is at the moment, do you?' and I said I thought she was at Markham's, but her mum said she wasn't. She said she had got home at two o'clock and found the letter waiting and had taken it straight round to Markham's for Jessamy to open, 'And they told me she'd gone off at one.'

I said, 'Oh,' not being able to think of anything else. So then Jessamy's mum said, 'And what about

152

Thursday evening?' and I said, 'Thursday evening?'
in a totally blank sort of voice, thinking to myself that
Jessamy didn't have to work on Thursday evenings
but not liking to say so in case for some reason that
was what she had told her mum.

Her mum said, 'She doesn't work on Thursday
evenings, does she? I've only just found out. She led
me to believe that she did . . . right through until seven
o'clock.'

I didn't know what to say to that, nor when her
mum asked me if I thought Jessamy had anything to
hide. I lamely muttered something about boyfriends
but that was the wrong thing, too, because I could tell
her mum was remembering the time she'd gone out
with Ginny's cousin and they'd gone ice skating and
she'd injured herself.

I really wasn't able to be of any help at all which
made me feel quite guilty after all that Jessamy's mum
has done for me, giving me free dancing lessons right
at the beginning. If it hadn't been for her I would
never have got into ballet school, and now she is dead
worried about Jessamy, who is supposed to be my
best friend, and I couldn't say one single thing to put
her mind at rest, just made matters worse by talking
about money and about boyfriends.

PS Maggot and Nella rang. They have both been
asked back.

PPS Next week I shall see Paco!

I do wish I knew what Jessamy was up to. Please
God it isn't anything bad!

It was four o'clock when Jessamy arrived home.

'Mum?' She put her head round the door of the sitting room. 'Was there any post? Did my letter come?'

Belinda Tarrant was on her own. She switched off the television and turned slowly to face her daughter.

'Yes,' she said, 'it came. Here you are.' She held it out. 'You might as well open it.'

Jessamy slit the envelope with her fingernail in her usual happy-go-lucky (exuberant?) fashion. Belinda Tarrant watched her, closely.

'Mum!' Jessamy's face broke into a triumphant beam. 'I've been asked back!'

'So I should hope.' Her mum said it quite calmly, quite matter-of-factly. 'I would not have expected anything else.'

'No, but it's always a bit tense-making,' said Jessamy.

'Is it? In that case it's a pity you weren't here earlier ... you could have spared yourself several hours of anxiety. I did actually take the trouble,' said Belinda Tarrant, 'to call in at Markham's with it for you, but I was too late. They told me you stopped working at one.'

'Oh! Yes.' Two rose-tipped fingers stole across Jessamy's cheeks leaving a trail of blushing pink. 'Yes, I – I do. On a Saturday.'

'You didn't tell me.'

'Um – no. Didn't I?'

'No, you didn't. So where have you been, or should I not ask?'

'I've been up to town,' said Jessamy.

154

'You've been up to town. Is that where you went on Thursday, as well?'

'Thursday.' The fingers stole back again, and this time the trail they left was a glowing fire of crimson. 'Um – yes,' said Jessamy.

'Do you mind telling me what you've been doing up there?'

This is it, thought Jessamy. The moment she had been waiting for – and dreading. *El momento de la verdad!*

'Well?' Belinda Tarrant said it pleasantly enough, but there was a definite edge to her voice.

'Well!' Jessamy gulped. 'Well, I – I – '

'Jessamy, I think there is something you should know.' Belinda Tarrant reached out a hand for her bag. She took something out of it and held it up: Jessamy's building society book. 'I found this today. I couldn't understand why you seemed so desperate to work when we can hardly be said to keep you short of money.'

There was a pause.

'What's happened to it all, Jessamy? What have you been spending it on?'

'I – ' Jessamy's throat had gone very dry. She swallowed, trying to find a voice to speak with. 'I – '

'You're not on drugs, are you?'

'Oh, Mum! Please!'

The relief on Belinda Tarrant's face was plain to see.

'Is that what you thought?' said Jessamy. '*Honestly*?'

Her mum shook her head. 'I didn't know what to

think. I know it's your money, to do what you like with – but there was an awful lot of it, Jessamy!'

'Dancing lessons cost a lot,' muttered Jessamy.

'What?' Belinda Tarrant said it sharply. 'Dancing lessons? What are you talking about?'

'Spanish dancing . . . I've been learning Spanish dancing! Mum, that's what I want to do! More than anything! I was going to tell you just as soon as I'd got my letter . . . I was just waiting for everything to be all right, so's you'd know I wasn't letting you down . . . so's you'd know that I *could* have stayed on if – '

'Could?' Belinda Tarrant was sounding rather dazed.

'Well, yes, if that was what I wanted. But, Mum, it isn't! I w- '

'Jessamy! Just stop a moment. You're confusing me. Where have you been learning this – this so-called Spanish dancing?'

'It's not so-called, it's real! It's flamenco! I looked in one of your dance magazines and I found this place near Covent Garden, La Escuela de Baile Español – '

'Pardon?' said Belinda Tarrant.

'La Escuela de Baile Español. Mum, it's really good! There's this wonderful teacher, Rafael de Lucia, he's quite old, about seventy, I should think, and he wouldn't take me at first, not until he'd seen me dance, 'cause he's like you, he doesn't take just anyone, he only wants people with potential, and Mum, that's what I've got! He says – '

Belinda Tarrant stood up.

'Before you tell me what he says, Jessamy, I think that we had better call your father down.'

Jessamy had hoped her dad might be a bit less hostile than her mum – after all, he was the one who had defended Spanish dancing. It seemed, however, that while it was all right for Spaniards and 'other people' it was not all right for the daughter of Ben Hart and Belinda Tarrant.

'Are you out of your mind?' He stood, legs apart, hands on hips, subjecting Jessamy to a piercing glare. 'Have you taken leave of your senses?'

'Dad, I – '

'All that stamping and banging! It'll ruin you for ballet!'

'I think what she's trying to convey to us – ' Belinda Tarrant spoke in dry, harsh tones – 'is that she wants to leave the ballet and take up Spanish dancing instead.'

'*What*?' Ben Hart was leaning forward, craning his neck as if he hadn't heard aright. 'Did you say, take up Spanish dancing?'

'Dad, I'm good at it! I really am!'

'You're good at ballet!' roared her dad. He suddenly stopped. His eyes narrowed. 'You're not saying you haven't been kept on? Is that what you're saying?'

'She's been kept on.'

'Then what – ? I don't understand! How can you want to leave?'

'Dad, I've found something I like better – something I can *do* better. Something no one else in the family has done!'

157

'No one else in the family has become a coal heaver! Maybe you'd rather do that?'

Jessamy gnawed at her lower lip. She had known this wasn't going to be easy.

'To throw up years of training on a mere passing whim – '

'Dad! It's not a passing whim! It's something I really, really want to do!'

'You might really really want to become a concert pianist or a – ' her dad threw up his hands – 'or a leading soprano at the Sydney Opera House! It's not a question of really really wanting but of really really having the ability. For crying out loud! Kids in some parts of Spain live and breathe flamenco from the very moment they're born! What chance do you think you'd stand? It's like someone at the age of eighteen suddenly taking it into their head they'd really really like to be a ballet dancer. Well, no way! You can't just go waltzing into these things!'

'I know that,' said Jessamy. She wasn't stupid! 'But I've already been trained as a dancer. Mr de Lucia – '

'Who in the name of all that's wonderful is Mr de Lucia?'

'Rafael de Lucia, he's – '

'The dancer?'

'Yes! I've been having lessons from him. And he says that because I've already been trained it should be quite easy for me to switch over. He says it might be different if I'd never had any lessons at all, but – '

'Twelve years of them! All for nothing!'

That was her mum. Her dad was looking at her, frown lines between his eyes.

'Rafael de Lucia has been teaching you?'

'Yes, and I've got potential, Dad, I know I have!' Jessamy said it fervently, desperately trying to convey to them both how important it was, this new thing in her life. 'Speak to Mr de Lucia! Speak to Mr Badowski! Speak to Saul! Sp- '

'Saul?' Belinda Tarrant was thrown off balance. 'What does Saul know about it?'

'He's seen me dance!'

'When?'

'On the train – ' Jessamy faltered. 'C-coming back from B-Bath.'

'On the train coming back from Bath?' Her mum snorted, derisively. Jessamy munched hard on her lip. 'Seeing someone dance on a train is scarcely what I should call much of a recommendation!'

'Why?' Jessamy rallied. She felt suddenly strong. Suddenly defiant. This was her future and she was going to fight for it! 'Why isn't it much of a recommendation? Saul was the one who told you about Karen! She hadn't had a single ballet lesson but he knew that she was good. So why shouldn't he know whether I am?'

Belinda Tarrant considered her, irritably. Jessamy had scored a point by bringing Saul into it. Her mum trusted Saul's judgement. She would listen to him.

'Is he a party to all this?' she said. 'Is he aware of what you've been up to?'

'No.' Jessamy shook her head. 'I haven't told anyone. Not even Karen. But Mr de Lu- '

'If I hear that man's name again I shall scream!'

'But Mr de Lucia – '

'Was one of the all-time greats.' Jessamy's dad said it in a voice devoid of expression. 'A famous exponent of the art.'

'*Art*? What *art*?'

'Flamenco dancing. It is an art, however you may choose to think of it. If he believes Jessamy has potential – '

'And Saul!' cried Jessamy.

A slight grim smile flickered across her dad's features. 'And Saul, of course. We mustn't forget Saul. If *Saul* and Mr de Lucia believe Jessamy has potential, then you may rest assured that she has.'

'So what are you saying?' Belinda Tarrant turned, rather helplessly, to her husband. 'Are you saying we should encourage her?'

'Why ask me? Ask the experts! Saul – and Mr de Lucia.'

'You think I should ring him?'

'Saul? Or – '

'Saul!' snapped Belinda Tarrant.

Jessamy's dad humped a shoulder. 'You must do as you think fit. I wash my hands of it.'

'Mum?' said Jessamy.

'Wait there.'

Belinda Tarrant left the room. Jessamy and her dad stood awkwardly staring at each other.

'Might as well sit down,' said her dad.

They sat.

'Do you feel we've pushed you?' he said. 'Is that what it is?'

'Not – pushed, exactly,' said Jessamy. 'It's just – '

'What?'

She gestured. 'Like always living in somebody's shadow!'

There was a long silence.

'I see,' said her dad.

At least he didn't still sound mad at her, so that was a hopeful sign.

After a few minutes, her mum came back.

'I've spoken to Saul,' she said. 'He's still on the phone, you'd better go and have a word with him.'

'Me?' said Jessamy.

She went out, apprehensively, into the hall and picked up the telephone.

'Saul?'

'You?'

'Mum said to come and have a word.'

'The things you drag me into,' said Saul.

'What did you tell her?' whispered Jessamy.

'Told her you were brilliant, didn't I?'

'*Truly*?'

'Truly. And truthfully. I was really impressed by your display of espanish *fuego*! I knew damn well Alex Badowski wasn't responsible for it.'

'So what did – ' Jessamy cupped a hand over her mouth. 'What did Mum say?'

'You really want to know?'

'Yes! Tell me!'

'She gave this long-suffering sigh and said, "I suppose we shall have to let her have her own way." '

'Oh, *yikes*!' screamed Jessamy.

161

Sunday 24 July

Jessamy came round this morning. I can't believe it! She says she is going to be a Spanish dancer! She has been secretly taking lessons all this time and now she has broken the news to her parents and they have said that maybe she can go to Spain and study full time instead of coming back to ballet school.

It was going to see Carlos Miguel that did it. She said she knew right from that very first night that it was what she wanted to do. She just had to find out if she was any good at it. And of course she is. I am going to miss her dreadfully but if it's what she really wants then I ought to be happy for her. I am happy for her. Oh, but it's going to be so strange and lonely when she is no longer here! I can't imagine life on my own, without Jessamy. She promises that she will write but it won't be the same. I will have to learn to stand on my own two feet and not always rely on Jessamy to push me into doing things. It will probably be good for me, but that doesn't mean that I am going to like it. I shall just grit my teeth and think very hard of dancing. After all, it is the only thing that really matters in life.

Monday 25 July

Today I had this sudden thought: suppose Jessamy were to join Carlos Miguel's company and dance with Paco? I don't think I could bear it!

11

I am desolate. Life has lost all meaning. Paco has gone. He has left the Company and I shall never see him again.

Oh, and I was so looking forward to it! Jessamy and I had booked tickets for both the afternoon and the evening performances, which meant Jessamy missing one of her classes with Rafael de Lucia, but she said he didn't mind as it would all be good experience for her.

I spent ages and ages deciding what to wear, trying on practically everything in my wardrobe, although that is not in truth very much. I also washed my hair which at last, thank goodness, is back to normal, and this time I was really determined that I would say something to Paco even if it was only just to smile and say hallo.

Jessamy said that she was definitely going to talk to him. She was going to be cheeky and say that she had seen him on the train. She was also going to tell him about how he had helped inspire her to take Spanish dancing classes. I actually had these visions that maybe, because of Jessamy going to be a Spanish dancer, he would suggest that we went to have a coffee together. And I thought that perhaps one of the others, like Pepe Ruiz or Luis Martín, would come with us and that they would fancy Jessamy and Paco would fancy me and we would all go on to a disco (I have never been to a disco!) and afterwards, when we were alone, Paco would tell me that his father was looking for a very English sort of dancer with fair hair to dance with Paco in some of the ballet-type numbers and would I be interested? And in my dream, of course, I said yes, and we all went off to Spain, and Jessamy joined the Company as well, only she danced with Pepe and Luis while I danced with Paco, and –

Oh, what is the point? Nothing like that is ever going to happen! Jessamy is going off to Spain and I am going back to ballet school and I am deathly, deathly miserable.

I suppose I should start at the beginning in case one day I want to look back and remember, though I cannot imagine I ever will. After all, who wants to remember being miserable? But this is meant to be a truthful account of my life so I will force myself to write it all down and relive it as it happened.

Right at the start I knew that something was wrong when Paco didn't appear all through the first performance. Jessamy suggested that maybe he'd been held back until the evening because as she said 'He is one of the stars.' And it is true that the stars do not always dance at matinées, and so I kept telling myself this and trying very hard not to be worried though naturally I was bitterly disappointed. But then he wasn't in the evening performance either, not even when Maria Rojas was, who he usually dances with, so that by the end of the evening I had to accept that he was not going to appear and I just wanted to sit and weep only of course I couldn't but had to clap and clap and smile and smile and try my best to pretend that my heart wasn't breaking even though it was.

Jessamy said to me, 'I expect he's gone and injured himself,' trying to cheer me up I think, though I'm not sure what was supposed to be cheering about it considering that Saturday was the last night and my very last chance to see him. On the other hand at least I would then have known that he was still with the Company and that maybe one day they would come back and I could see him again, whereas as it is I probably never will.

We went round to the stage door afterwards. I didn't want to, I just wanted to get home so that I could crawl into bed and howl, but Jessamy insisted. She said, 'I'll find out what's happened to him, don't you worry!' and she went and planted herself right at the front of the crowd, dragging me with her, and when Luis came out she waved at him and he saw her and smiled and came over, and Jessamy said, 'Where's Paco?' and Luis said, 'He no with us no more' and my heart just turned over and I really thought I was going to faint.

So then Jessamy said, 'What, you mean he's left?' and Luis said, 'Sí! He left,' and then he grinned and said, 'I very sorry! I know you like,' and Jessamy got a bit huffed on account of never falling prey to that sort of passion, which she thinks is soppy, but at least she didn't give me away, which she could have done, but just said rather haughtily, 'That's a pity. I wanted to tell him that I'm going to Spain to study Spanish

165

dancing,' at which Luis raised both his eyebrows and grinned again, so that you could tell he didn't take her seriously and thought she was just another besotted fan, and that got Jessamy really mad.

She said, 'So where has he gone? Has he joined another company?' and if I hadn't been feeling so utterly devastated I think I would have laughed because she sounded just like Madam at her frostiest. But Luis only hunched his shoulders up to his ears and said 'No sé' which comes from the verb 'saber', which I have just been learning. It means, 'I don't know.' And then he added that nadie knew, which I thought perhaps meant that someone called Nadia could tell us and as we moved away I started to nag at Jessamy and say why hadn't she found out who this Nadia was so that we could ask her, but she explained it wasn't a person's name but simply means 'nobody'. Nobody knows. So that is that.

On the way home Jessamy said, 'I knew I shouldn't have listened to you.' I said, 'What do you mean?' and she said, 'That day on the train . . . if you'd let me talk to him he might have told us where he was going.' I said gloomily that he probably wouldn't have known since it sounded to me as if he'd had another row with his father and just stormed out, which isn't the sort of thing that you necessarily plan but the sort of thing you do on the spur of the moment. I said, 'I am doomed to worship from afar,' and Jessamy giggled (she can be very unfeeling) and said, 'Yes, you are, if you keep refusing to go and talk to people.'

But what could I have talked to Paco about? You

166

can't just go up to someone who has no idea who you are and start saying things.

Actually that is not true. Jessamy can. But I am not Jessamy!

I wish that I were. She is so happy and confident, especially now that she has got her own way about the Spanish dancing. Will I ever be confident? Will I ever be happy? Oh, why am I so dumb?

Sunday 4 September
I have not felt like writing anything in this diary just recently, I have been too miserable. I keep looking at my photographs of Paco and at his autograph that Jessamy got for me and having these beautiful day-dreams which I know are just ridiculous and can never come true.

Today I said goodbye to Jessamy. In the morning she is flying to Spain, to Madrid, to start full-time classes in Spanish dancing. She is staying with friends of her mum and dad, people that used to be dancers. I am going to miss her terribly. She has promised to write, but it won't be the same as having her here.

Friday 9 September
On Monday I go back to ballet school. What am I going to do without Jessamy?

Postcard from Jessamy

Dear Karen,
Madrid is brilliant and so are my dancing classes. I am learning lots of Spanish, including swear

*words! I will watch out for Paco and let you know
if he turns up in a dance company over here.
Imagine if one day I got to dance with him! Proper
letter soon, I promise. Give my love to Nella and
Maggot. Don't forget to write to me!
xxx Jessamy.*

Letter from Karen

*Dear Jessamy,
Guess what? The most incredible and wonderful thing
has happened! I will have to tell you because even if
you were to guess from here till the end of time you
wouldn't ever guess right!*

*On Monday we started back at CBS and to be
truthful I was dreading it a bit because of you not
being there. It is very strange, very quiet, without you.
Maggot and Nella send their love and so do lots of
other people but Ginny I think is secretly quite pleased
that you have left because it means she hasn't got a
rival any more and is probably imagining that she
can step into your shoes, which she most certainly
cannot. However, that is not the incredible and wonderful thing! The incredible and wonderful thing
occurred almost the very minute that I got there.*

*This is what happened. I was walking up the steps
of the students' entrance and there was this boy
ahead of me, black-haired and wearing jeans and
boots, and he seemed familiar but I couldn't think
why, and then at the top of the steps he turned and
looked back and oh, Jessamy, you will never guess!
It was Paco!!! And he recognised me! He shot out a*

168

finger, almost like accusing, and said, 'I see you before!' and I nearly died because I thought he meant at the stage door, but he didn't. Jessamy, he's seen me dance! He came to our performance at the Fountain, just before we went to Bath, and he remembered!

I am so bubbling over with happiness that I can't write cohesively or do I mean coherently? I expect you will have gathered this by now! I will try to explain things properly.

For a start you must be wondering what Paco is doing at ballet school. Well, believe it or not.he has actually been accepted as a graduate student! And today in pas de deux *Mr Calvert put us to dance together which means that* both *my heart's desires have now been fulfilled!!! I thought naturally I would be going to dance with John as usual, but Mr Calvert said Paco and I looked as if we would make a good team, what with him being so dark and me being fair. You can imagine that I nearly died for the second time!*

Oh, but I still haven't told you what he is doing at ballet school, have I? It is amazing but it is just like your story in reverse! You saw the Spanish ballet and immediately wanted to be a Spanish dancer, and Paco saw some classical ballet and immediately wanted to be a ballet dancer! Well, it didn't happen quite like that, it wasn't actually immediate because he first saw some ballet about five years ago and has been taking ballet lessons on and off ever since, and that was what all the rows with his father were about as Carlos Miguel thought he ought to stay with the Company and Paco didn't want to.

169

I told him about us hearing them having an argument in the hotel (you are right: tu madre is swearing!) and he said that was because Carlos Miguel was mad at him for coming to see us at the Fountain when he should have been doing something else, and that was when Paco finally made his decision. He said he'd already been for an audition with Madam and been offered a place but couldn't bring himself to tell Carlos Miguel. That night he did, and that was when the sparks flew! Carlos Miguel threatened that 'If you leave this company you leave for ever.' Paco says his father is a very violent person who is always flying into rages – but then he admitted that maybe he takes after him! He has promised, however, that if I will stay as his partner he will not fly into any rages with me.

Maggot, not knowing the way I feel, says he ought to dance with Ginny because then we would have some fun. Ginny is already complaining about his language. That is because she went shoving past him to get at the notice-board, you know the way she does, and he swore at her. Personally I think she deserved it. Maggot says she hopes he will do it again as it is time someone put Ginny in her place.

But isn't it odd, the way things work out? To think that there was Paco having a row with Carlos Miguel because he wanted to do ballet and you having to tell your mum that you wanted to do Spanish dancing, except of course your mum came round in the end while Paco's dad is still mad at him, but Paco says his dad is usually mad at him so there is nothing very peculiar in that.

170

I asked him by the way what all those words were that you said were rude, and he admitted that they were rude, just a little bit, but he won't say what they mean! I am going to keep on at him until he tells me.

He's staying at the YMCA at the moment but is looking for somewhere else except he hasn't got much money, only what he has managed to save up. He's working in the evenings as a waiter to pay his fees at CBS. I wish he could come and take a room with us! But Gran doesn't like having young people as lodgers, she says they are more trouble than they are worth, always coming in late and playing loud music and so on, and I must confess Paco is not what I would call a quiet sort of person. Maggot says he is dynamic. *(Ginny says he is a gypsy and uncouth and has no manners, but that is only because she is jealous.)*

I really must stop now as it is rather late as Maggot and I went to Paco's restaurant where he works and stayed to eat some spaghetti and talk to Paco who kept coming over to our table in between serving customers. When I got in Gran said, 'Karen it's half past ten!' shock horror as if I am Cinderella and all my clothes will turn to rags if I am not home by the witching hour, which for Gran is nine o'clock. I don't want to upset her but I think she has to realise that I am not a child any more.

Please write soon with all your news,
Love from Karen.

Postcard from Jessamy

Querida mía,
Your news was amazing!!! I am really glad that
you are happy because I am, too. You have no idea
what a relief it is, not having to fret all the time
about putting on extra kilos. Now I can have boobs,
like other people! And hips as well, if I want.
Hooray! No time for real letter but will write one
soon, I PROMISE. xxx Jessamy
PS Say olé to Paco for me and give him a big hug!

'That is from your friend?' demanded Paco.

'From Jessamy,' said Karen.

'The one I see on the train. The one that has gone
to Espain to learn how to dance the flamenco.' Paco
craned over Karen's shoulder to look at Jessamy's
card. 'What does this mean?' He pointed. 'What is
boobs?'

'Not telling you!' Karen slapped his hand away.
'Not until you tell me what all those other words
mean.'

Paco raised an eyebrow. 'Why? Is rude?'

'Not saying!' She pushed at him. 'Stop reading
other people's postcards!'

'But I wish to know what she say! I see my name
there. What does she say about me?'

'She says I'm to say *olé* to you.'

'Only that? I see more! I see where she say give
a big hug!'

Karen blushed.

'Is this not what she say?'

172

Reluctantly, she nodded.

'Hah!' Paco tapped out a triumphant drumbeat with his heels. He folded his arms. 'So! I wait!'

Karen hesitated. The door of the studio had swung open and Ginny and Lorraine had walked in. Ginny looked at Karen, sourly. She had recently decided to be mad at her because in spite of Paco swearing when she shoved him she reckoned she was the one he ought to be dancing with, not Karen. Karen, she said, was too namby-pamby. Too wishy-washy. Couldn't say boo to a goose. There would be nothing Ginny would relish more than a nice juicy bit of gossip.

'*Venga*!' Paco stamped a foot. He didn't give two straws for Ginny and Lorraine. 'Are you going to do what your friend tell you or not?'

Karen didn't give two straws for them, either. Before Ginny's supercilious gaze, she launched herself at him.

'Olé, Paco!'

Jessamy would have been proud of her!

Other great reads **from Red Fox**

Further Red Fox titles that you might enjoy reading are listed on the following pages. They are available in bookshops or they can be ordered directly from us.

  If you would like to order books, please send this form and the money due to:

ARROW BOOKS, BOOKSERVICE BY POST, PO BOX 29, DOUGLAS, ISLE OF MAN, BRITISH ISLES. Please enclose a cheque or postal order made out to Arrow Books Ltd for the amount due, plus 75p per book for postage and packing to a maximum of £7.50, both for orders within the UK. For customers outside the UK, please allow £1.00 per book.

NAME_____

ADDRESS_____

_____

Please print clearly.

Whilst every effort is made to keep prices low, it is sometimes necessary to increase cover prices at short notice. If you are ordering books by post, to save delay it is advisable to phone to confirm the correct price. The number to ring is THE SALES DEPARTMENT 0171 (if outside London) 973 9000.

Follow the traumas and triumphs of Jessamy and Karen as they pursue their dream of ballet stardom in the DANCING DREAMS sequence from Red Fox!

A DANCING DREAMS STORY – STAR TURN

Jessamy's dance-mad parents have brought her up to eat, drink and sleep ballet but she's never captured that special *something* in her dancing. So when Jessamy spots shy, new girl Karen, and sees in her a born dancer with masses of potential, she's determined to make sure her new friend's talents come under the spotlight – in her very own star turn . . .
ISBN 0 09 925091 8   £2.99

A DANCING DREAMS STORY – A DREAM COME TRUE

Jessamy and Karen's dreams seem to be coming true . . . they're *both* now attending the prestigious City Ballet School! There's no stopping Karen – she's a naturally gifted dancer and under the new training programme her talents really begin to shine. But while Karen glows with success, Jessamy battles with feelings of jealousy – and is more determined than ever *not* to be just a 'nobody' . . .
ISBN 0 09 925101 9   £2.99

A DANCING DREAMS STORY – FANDANGO!

Jessamy and Karen are now closer to the big time than ever before – and they both know that discipline is the key to success in professional ballet. But training suddenly takes a back seat when Karen falls head over heels in love with a dream-boat guy and Jessamy discovers the thrills of Spanish dancing. Will the girls' new-found passions force them to abandon ballet for ever? . . .
ISBN 0 09 925111 6   £2.99